STUDENT LECTURE NOTEBOOK

McMURRY FAY

Chemistry

FOURTH EDITION

Upper Saddle River, NJ 07458

Project Manager: Kristen Kaiser
Senior Editor: Kent Porter-Hamann
Editor-in-Chief, Science: John Challice
Vice President of Production & Manufacturing: David W. Riccardi
Executive Managing Editor: Kathleen Schiaparelli
Assistant Managing Editor: Becca Richter
Production Editor: Rhonda Aversa
Supplement Cover Management/Design: Paul Gourhan
Manufacturing Buyer: Ilene Kahn

© 2004 Pearson Education, Inc.
Pearson Prentice Hall
Pearson Education, Inc.
Upper Saddle River, NJ 07458

Printed in the United States of America

10 9 8 7 6 5 4 3 2

ISBN 0-13-142509-9

Pearson Education Ltd., *London*
Pearson Education Australia Pty. Ltd., *Sydney*
Pearson Education Singapore, Pte. Ltd.
Pearson Education North Asia Ltd., *Hong Kong*
Pearson Education Canada, Inc., *Toronto*
Pearson Educación de Mexico, S.A. de C.V.
Pearson Education—Japan, *Tokyo*
Pearson Education Malaysia, Pte. Ltd.
Pearson Education, *Upper Saddle River, New Jersey*

TABLE OF CONTENTS

Chapter 6

Chapter 7

Chapter 8

Chapter 9

Chapter 17

Chapter 18

Chapter 19

Chapter 20

1

Chemistry: Matter and Measurement

Relative abundance on Earth

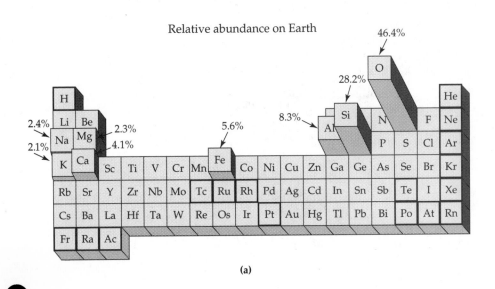

(a)

Relative abundance in the human body

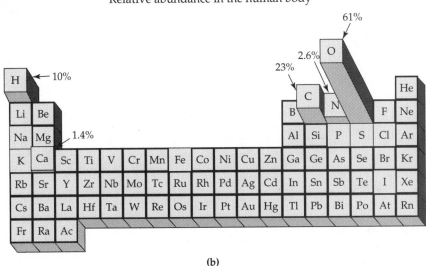

(b)

FIGURE 1.1   Elemental composition of the Earth's crust and the human body

Main groups

Main groups

Period	1 1A																	18 8A
1	1 H	2 2A	Transition metal groups										13 3A	14 4A	15 5A	16 6A	17 7A	2 He
2	3 Li	4 Be											5 B	6 C	7 N	8 O	9 F	10 Ne
3	11 Na	12 Mg	3 3B	4 4B	5 5B	6 6B	7 7B	8	9 8B	10	11 1B	12 2B	13 Al	14 Si	15 P	16 S	17 Cl	18 Ar
4	19 K	20 Ca	21 Sc	22 Ti	23 V	24 Cr	25 Mn	26 Fe	27 Co	28 Ni	29 Cu	30 Zn	31 Ga	32 Ge	33 As	34 Se	35 Br	36 Kr
5	37 Rb	38 Sr	39 Y	40 Zr	41 Nb	42 Mo	43 Tc	44 Ru	45 Rh	46 Pd	47 Ag	48 Cd	49 In	50 Sn	51 Sb	52 Te	53 I	54 Xe
6	55 Cs	56 Ba	57 La	72 Hf	73 Ta	74 W	75 Re	76 Os	77 Ir	78 Pt	79 Au	80 Hg	81 Tl	82 Pb	83 Bi	84 Po	85 At	86 Rn
7	87 Fr	88 Ra	89 Ac	104 Rf	105 Db	106 Sg	107 Bh	108 Hs	109 Mt	110	111	112		114		116		

Lanthanides	58 Ce	59 Pr	60 Nd	61 Pm	62 Sm	63 Eu	64 Gd	65 Tb	66 Dy	67 Ho	68 Er	69 Tm	70 Yb	71 Lu
Actinides	90 Th	91 Pa	92 U	93 Np	94 Pu	95 Am	96 Cm	97 Bk	98 Cf	99 Es	100 Fm	101 Md	102 No	103 Lr

Metals   Semimetals   Nonmetals

FIGURE 1.2 The modern form of the periodic table

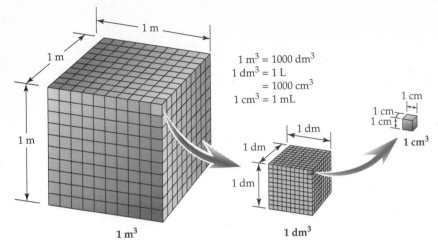

$1\ m^3 = 1000\ dm^3$
$1\ dm^3 = 1\ L$
$\quad\quad = 1000\ cm^3$
$1\ cm^3 = 1\ mL$

1 m³

1 dm³

1 cm³

FIGURE 1.5   A cubic meter

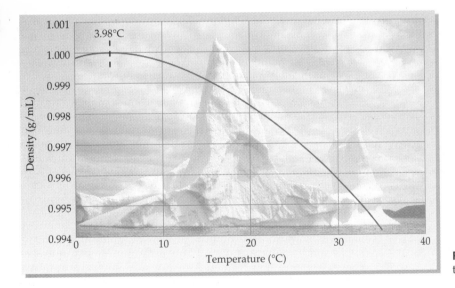

FIGURE 1.7   The density of water at different temperatures

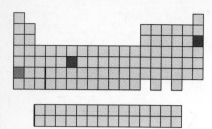

Key Concept Question 1.22   Is the element marked in red on the following periodic table likely to be a gas, a liquid, or a solid? What is the atomic number of the element in blue? Name at least one other element that is chemically similar to the element in green.

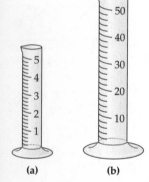

(a)   (b)

Key Concept Question 1.26   Assume that you have two graduated cylinders, one with a capacity of 5 mL (a) and the other with a capacity of 50 mL (b). Draw a line in each, showing how much liquid you would add if you needed to measure 2.64 mL of water. Which cylinder will give the more accurate measurement? Explain.

Chapter 2

Atoms, Molecules, and Ions

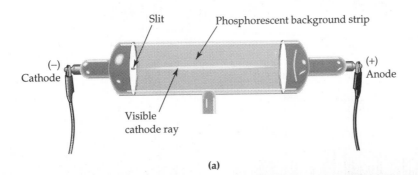

Slit   Phosphorescent background strip

(−)
Cathode

(+)
Anode

Visible
cathode ray

(a)

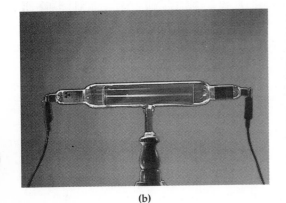

(b)

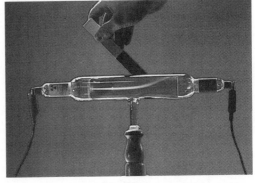

(c)

FIGURE 2.3
A cathode-ray tube

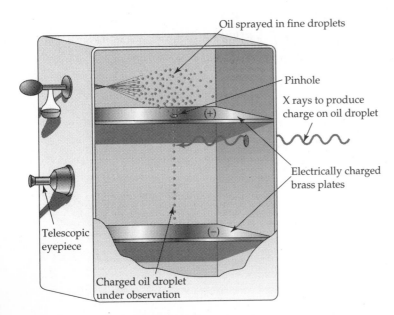

Oil sprayed in fine droplets

Pinhole

X rays to produce
charge on oil droplet

(+)

Electrically charged
brass plates

(−)

Telescopic
eyepiece

Charged oil droplet
under observation

FIGURE 2.4   Millikan's oil-drop experiment

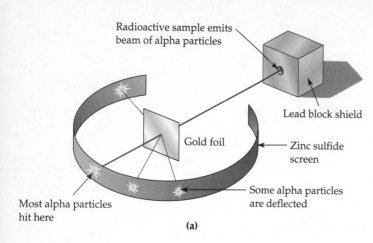

Radioactive sample emits beam of alpha particles

Lead block shield

Gold foil

Zinc sulfide screen

Some alpha particles are deflected

Most alpha particles hit here

(a)

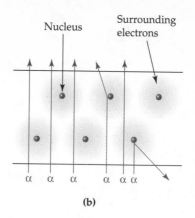

Nucleus

Surrounding electrons

α   α   α   α   α α

(b)

FIGURE 2.5
The Rutherford scattering experiment

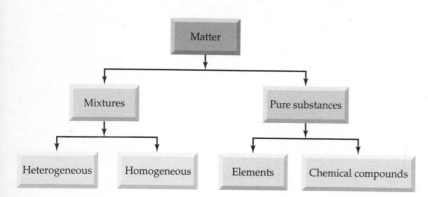

Matter

Mixtures

Pure substances

Heterogeneous

Homogeneous

Elements

Chemical compounds

FIGURE 2.7   A scheme for the classification of matter

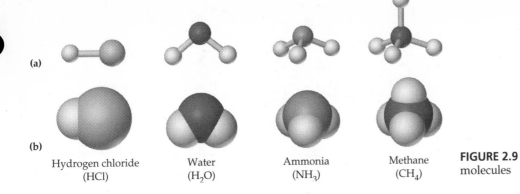

(a)

(b)

| Hydrogen chloride (HCl) | Water (H₂O) | Ammonia (NH₃) | Methane (CH₄) |

FIGURE 2.9   Visualizing some simple molecules

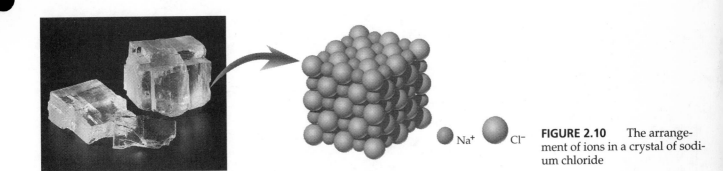

FIGURE 2.10   The arrangement of ions in a crystal of sodium chloride

1 1A													18 8A
H$^+$ **H$^-$** Hydride	2 2A			13 3A	14 4A	15 5A	16 6A	17 7A					
Li$^+$	Be^{2+}					N^{3-} Nitride	O^{2-} Oxide	F$^-$ Fluoride					
Na$^+$	Mg^{2+}			Al^{3+}			S^{2-} Sulfide	Cl$^-$ Chloride					
K$^+$	Ca^{2+}			Ga^{3+}			Se^{2-} Selenide	Br$^-$ Bromide					
Rb$^+$	Sr^{2+}			In^{3+}	Sn^{2+} Sn^{4+}		Te^{2-} Telluride	I$^-$ Iodide					
Cs$^+$	Ba^{2+}			Tl$^+$ Tl^{3+}	Pb^{2+} Pb^{4+}								

FIGURE 2.11   Main group cations and anions

3 3B	4 4B	5 5B	6 6B	7 7B	8	9 8B	10	11 1B	12 2B	
Sc^{3+}	Ti^{3+}	V^{3+}	Cr^{2+} Cr^{3+}	Mn^{2+}	Fe^{2+} Fe^{3+}	Co^{2+}	Ni^{2+}	Cu^{2+}	Zn^{2+}	
Y^{3+}					Ru^{3+}	Rh^{3+}	Pd^{2+}	Ag$^+$	Cd^{2+}	
La^{3+}									Hg^{2+}	

FIGURE 2.12 Common transition metal ions

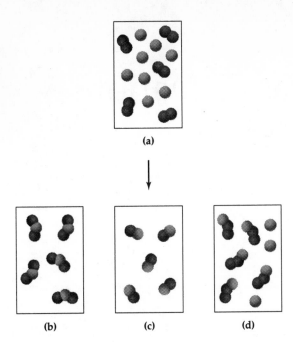

Key Concept Question 2.26 Assume that the mixture of substances in drawing (a) undergoes a reaction. Which of the drawings (b)–(d) represents a product mixture consistent with the law of mass conservation?

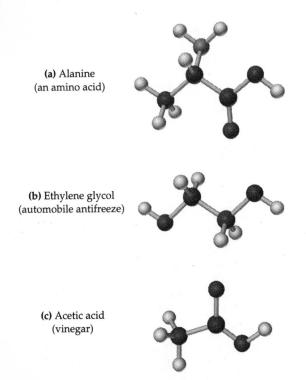

(a) Alanine
(an amino acid)

(b) Ethylene glycol
(automobile antifreeze)

(c) Acetic acid
(vinegar)

Key Concept Question 2.28 Give molecular formulas corresponding to each of the following ball-and-stick molecular representations (red = O, gray = C, blue = N, ivory = H). In writing the formula, list the atoms in alphabetical order.

Chapter 3

Formulas, Equations, and Moles

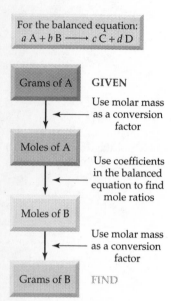

For the balanced equation:
$a\,A + b\,B \longrightarrow c\,C + d\,D$

Grams of A — **GIVEN**

Use molar mass as a conversion factor

Moles of A

Use coefficients in the balanced equation to find mole ratios

Moles of B

Use molar mass as a conversion factor

Grams of B — FIND

FIGURE 3.2 Conversions between moles and grams

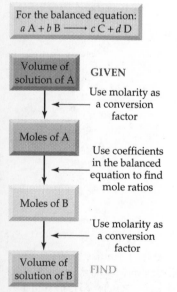

For the balanced equation:
$a\,A + b\,B \longrightarrow c\,C + d\,D$

Volume of solution of A — **GIVEN**

Use molarity as a conversion factor

Moles of A

Use coefficients in the balanced equation to find mole ratios

Moles of B

Use molarity as a conversion factor

Volume of solution of B — FIND

FIGURE 3.5 The use of molarity as a conversion factor

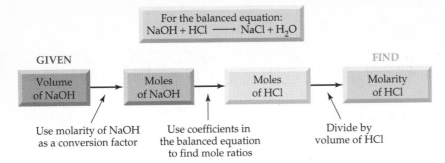

Use molarity of NaOH
as a conversion factor

Use coefficients in
the balanced equation
to find mole ratios

Divide by
volume of HCl

FIGURE 3.6   Procedure for acid–base titration

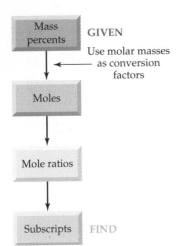

FIGURE 3.8   Calculating a formula from percent composition

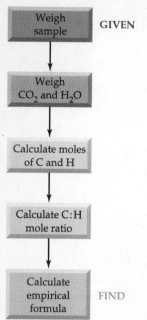

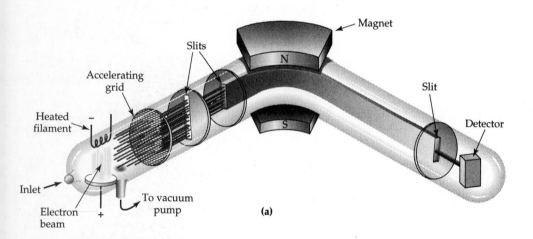

FIGURE 3.9 Determining an empirical formula from combustion analysis

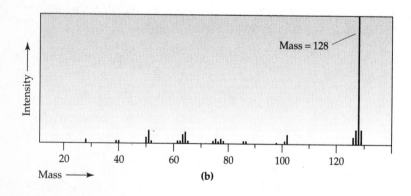

FIGURE 3.10 A mass spectrometer

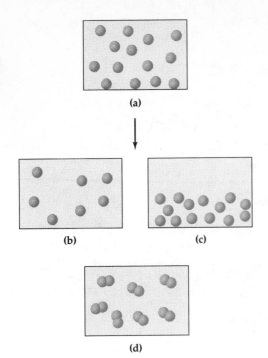

(a)

(b) (c)

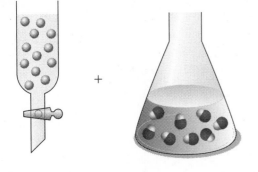

(d)

Key Concept Question 3.30 Box (a) represents 1.0 mL of a solution of particles at a given concentration. Which of the boxes (b)–(d) represents 1.0 mL of the solution that results after (a) has been diluted by doubling the volume of its solvent?

Key Concept Question 3.35 Assume that the buret contains H^+ ions, the flask contains OH^- ions, and you are carrying out a titration of the base with the acid. If the volumes in the buret and the flask are identical and the concentration of the acid in the buret is 1.00 M, what is the concentration of base in the flask?

Chapter 4

Reactions in Aqueous Solution

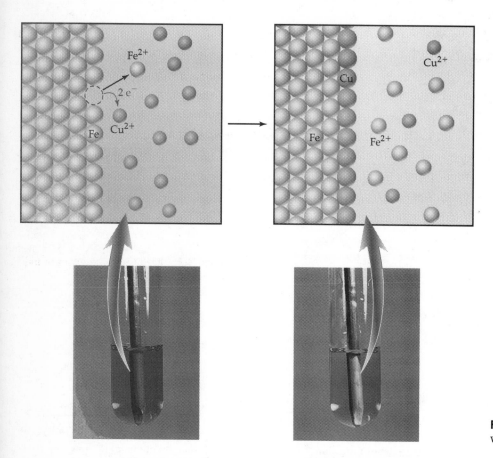

FIGURE 4.2 Redox reaction of iron with Cu^{2+} ions

TABLE 4.3	A Partial Activity Series of the Elements

Oxidation Reaction

Strongly reducing

$Li \rightarrow Li^+ + e^-$
$K \rightarrow K^+ + e^-$
$Ba \rightarrow Ba^{2+} + 2\,e^-$
$Ca \rightarrow Ca^{2+} + 2\,e^-$
$Na \rightarrow Na^+ + e^-$

These elements react rapidly with aqueous H^+ ions (acid) or with liquid H_2O to release H_2 gas.

$Mg \rightarrow Mg^{2+} + 2\,e^-$
$Al \rightarrow Al^{3+} + 3\,e^-$
$Mn \rightarrow Mn^{2+} + 2\,e^-$
$Zn \rightarrow Zn^{2+} + 2\,e^-$
$Cr \rightarrow Cr^{3+} + 3\,e^-$
$Fe \rightarrow Fe^{2+} + 2\,e^-$

These elements react with aqueous H^+ ions or with steam to release H_2 gas.

$Co \rightarrow Co^{2+} + 2\,e^-$
$Ni \rightarrow Ni^{2+} + 2\,e^-$
$Sn \rightarrow Sn^{2+} + 2\,e^-$

These elements react with aqueous H^+ ions to release H_2 gas.

$H_2 \rightarrow 2\,H^+ + 2\,e^-$

$Cu \rightarrow Cu^{2+} + 2\,e^-$
$Ag \rightarrow Ag^+ + e^-$
$Hg \rightarrow Hg^{2+} + 2\,e^-$
$Pt \rightarrow Pt^{2+} + 2\,e^-$
$Au \rightarrow Au^{3+} + 3\,e^-$

These elements do not react with aqueous H^+ ions to release H_2.

Weakly reducing

TABLE 4.3 Partial activity series of the elements

Step 1. Write the unbalanced net ionic equation.

Step 2. Balance the equation for all atoms other than H and O.

Step 3. Assign oxidation numbers to all atoms.

Step 4. Decide which atoms have changed oxidation number, and by how much.

Step 5. Make the total increase in oxidation number for oxidized atoms equal to the total decrease in oxidation number for reduced atoms.

Step 6. Balance the equation for O by adding water to the side with less O, and then balance for H by adding H^+ to the side with less H.

Check your answer by making sure the equation is balanced both for atoms and for charge.

FIGURE 4.3 Balancing redox equations by the oxidation-number method

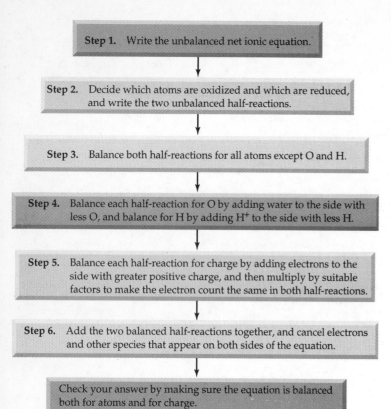

FGURE 4.4 Balancing redox equations by the half-reaction method

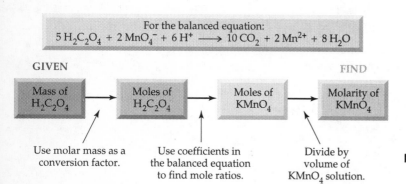

FIGURE 4.5 Flow diagram for a redox titration

Key Concept Question 4.24   Assume that an aqueous solution of a cation, represented as a red sphere, is allowed to mix with a solution of an anion, represented as a yellow sphere. Three possible outcomes are represented by boxes (1)–(3):

Which outcome corresponds to each of the following reactions?

(a) $2\,Na^+(aq) + CO_3{}^{2-}(aq) \rightarrow$

(b) $Ba^{2+}(aq) + CrO_4{}^{2-}(aq) \rightarrow$

(c) $2\,Ag^+(aq) + SO_3{}^{2-}(aq) \rightarrow$

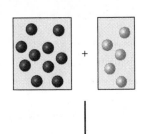

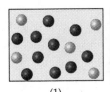 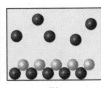 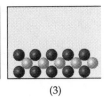

(1)   (2)   (3)

Key Concept Question 4.26   Assume that an aqueous solution of OH^-, represented as a blue sphere, is allowed to mix with a solution of an acid H_nA, represented as a red sphere. Three possible outcomes are depicted by boxes (1)–(3), where the green spheres represent A^{n-}, the anion of the acid:

Which outcome corresponds to each of the following reactions?

(a) $HF + OH^- \rightarrow H_2O + F^-$

(b) $H_2SO_3 + 2\,OH^- \rightarrow 2\,H_2O + SO_3{}^{2-}$

(c) $H_3PO_4 + 3\,OH^- \rightarrow 3\,H_2O + PO_4{}^{3-}$

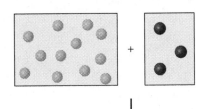

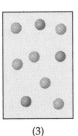

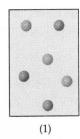 

(1)   (2)   (3)

Chapter 5

Periodicity and Atomic Structure

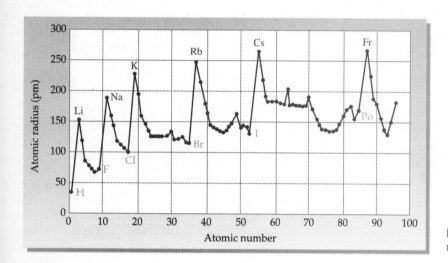

FIGURE 5.1   Atomic radius versus atomic number

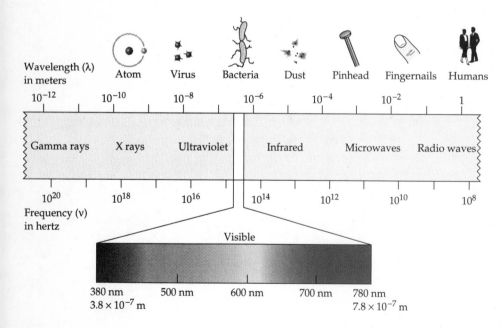

FIGURE 5.3   The electromagnetic spectrum

TABLE 5.2		Allowed Combinations of Quantum Numbers n, l, and m_l for the First Four Shells			
n	l	m_l	Orbital Notation	Number of Orbitals in Subshell	Number of Orbitals in Shell
1	0	0	1s	1	1
2	0	0	2s	1	4
	1	−1, 0, +1	2p	3	
3	0	0	3s	1	
	1	−1, 0, +1	3p	3	9
	2	−2, −1, 0, +1, +2	3d	5	
4	0	0	4s	1	
	1	−1, 0, +1	4p	3	16
	2	−2, −1, 0, +1, +2	4d	5	
	3	−3, −2, −1, 0, +1, +2, +3	4f	7	

TABLE 5.2   Quantum numbers for the first four shells

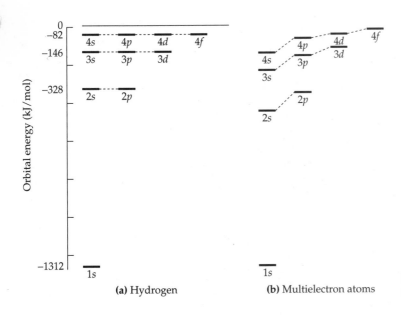

FIGURE 5.9   Orbital energy levels for hydrogen and a multielectron atom

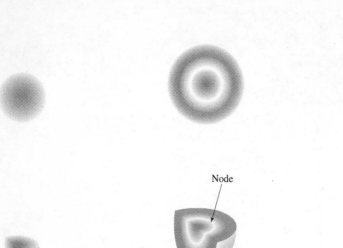

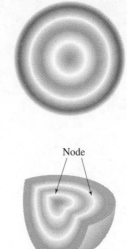

Node

Node

(a)   **(b)**   **(c)**

FIGURE 5.10
Representations of 1s, 2s, and 3s orbitals

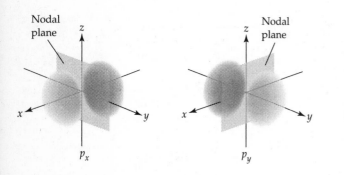

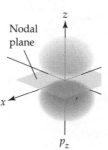

Nodal plane

Nodal plane

Nodal plane

p_x p_y p_z

FIGURE 5.12   The three 2p orbitals

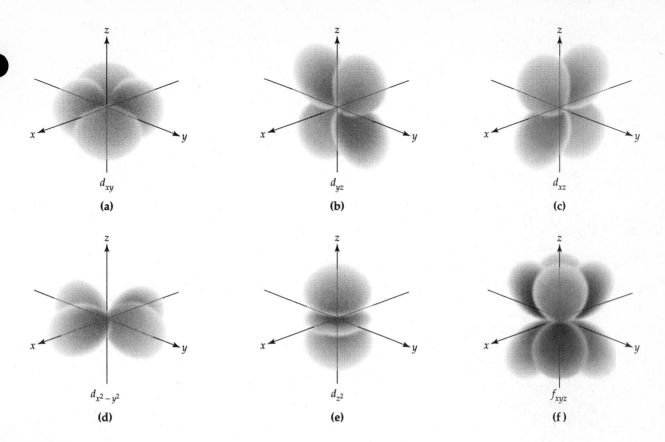

FIGURE 5.13 The five *3d* orbitals

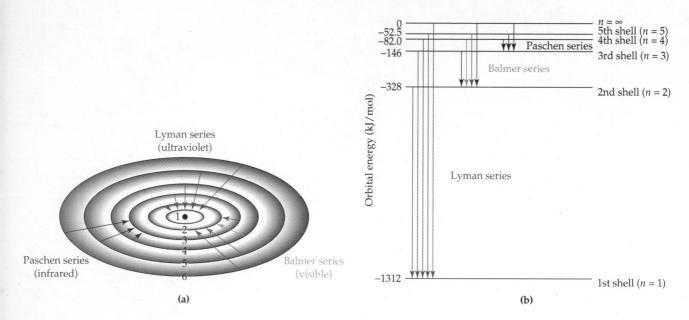

FIGURE 5.14 The origin of atomic line spectra

1 H $1s^1$																	2 He $1s^2$
3 Li $2s^1$	4 Be $2s^2$											5 B $2s^22p^1$	6 C $2s^22p^2$	7 N $2s^22p^3$	8 O $2s^22p^4$	9 F $2s^22p^5$	10 Ne $2s^22p^6$
11 Na $3s^1$	12 Mg $3s^2$											13 Al $3s^23p^1$	14 Si $3s^23p^2$	15 P $3s^23p^3$	16 S $3s^23p^4$	17 Cl $3s^23p^5$	18 Ar $3s^23p^6$
19 K $4s^1$	20 Ca $4s^2$	21 Sc $4s^23d^1$	22 Ti $4s^23d^2$	23 V $4s^23d^3$	24 Cr $4s^13d^5$	25 Mn $4s^23d^5$	26 Fe $4s^23d^6$	27 Co $4s^23d^7$	28 Ni $4s^23d^8$	29 Cu $4s^13d^{10}$	30 Zn $4s^23d^{10}$	31 Ga $4s^23d^{10}4p^1$	32 Ge $4s^23d^{10}4p^2$	33 As $4s^23d^{10}4p^3$	34 Se $4s^23d^{10}4p^4$	35 Br $4s^23d^{10}4p^5$	36 Kr $4s^23d^{10}4p^6$
37 Rb $5s^1$	38 Sr $5s^2$	39 Y $5s^24d^1$	40 Zr $5s^24d^2$	41 Nb $5s^14d^4$	42 Mo $5s^14d^5$	43 Tc $5s^24d^5$	44 Ru $5s^14d^7$	45 Rh $5s^14d^8$	46 Pd $4d^{10}$	47 Ag $5s^14d^{10}$	48 Cd $5s^24d^{10}$	49 In $5s^24d^{10}5p^1$	50 Sn $5s^24d^{10}5p^2$	51 Sb $5s^24d^{10}5p^3$	52 Te $5s^24d^{10}5p^4$	53 I $5s^24d^{10}5p^5$	54 Xe $5s^24d^{10}5p^6$
55 Cs $6s^1$	56 Ba $6s^2$	57 La $6s^25d^1$	72 Hf $6s^24f^{14}5d^2$	73 Ta $6s^24f^{14}5d^3$	74 W $6s^24f^{14}5d^4$	75 Re $6s^24f^{14}5d^5$	76 Os $6s^24f^{14}5d^6$	77 Ir $6s^24f^{14}5d^7$	78 Pt $6s^14f^{14}5d^9$	79 Au $6s^14f^{14}5d^{10}$	80 Hg $6s^24f^{14}5d^{10}$	81 Tl $6s^24f^{14}5d^{10}6p^1$	82 Pb $6s^24f^{14}5d^{10}6p^2$	83 Bi $6s^24f^{14}5d^{10}6p^3$	84 Po $6s^24f^{14}5d^{10}6p^4$	85 At $6s^24f^{14}5d^{10}6p^5$	86 Rn $6s^24f^{14}5d^{10}6p^6$
87 Fr $7s^1$	88 Ra $7s^2$	89 Ac $7s^26d^1$	104 Rf $7s^25f^{14}6d^2$	105 Db $7s^25f^{14}6d^3$	106 Sg $7s^25f^{14}6d^4$	107 Bh $7s^25f^{14}6d^5$	108 Hs $7s^25f^{14}6d^6$	109 Mt $7s^25f^{14}6d^7$	110 —	111 —	112 —		114 —		116 —		

58 Ce $6s^24f^15d^1$	59 Pr $6s^24f^3$	60 Nd $6s^24f^4$	61 Pm $6s^24f^5$	62 Sm $6s^24f^6$	63 Eu $6s^24f^7$	64 Gd $6s^24f^75d^1$	65 Tb $6s^24f^9$	66 Dy $6s^24f^{10}$	67 Ho $6s^24f^{11}$	68 Er $6s^24f^{12}$	69 Tm $6s^24f^{13}$	70 Yb $6s^24f^{14}$	71 Lu $6s^24f^{14}5d^1$
90 Th $7s^26d^2$	91 Pa $7s^25f^26d^1$	92 U $7s^25f^36d^1$	93 Np $7s^25f^46d^1$	94 Pu $7s^25f^6$	95 Am $7s^25f^7$	96 Cm $7s^25f^76d^1$	97 Bk $7s^25f^9$	98 Cf $7s^25f^{10}$	99 Es $7s^25f^{11}$	100 Fm $7s^25f^{12}$	101 Md $7s^25f^{13}$	102 No $7s^25f^{14}$	103 Lr $7s^25f^{14}6d^1$

FIGURE 5.17 Ground-state electron configurations of the elements

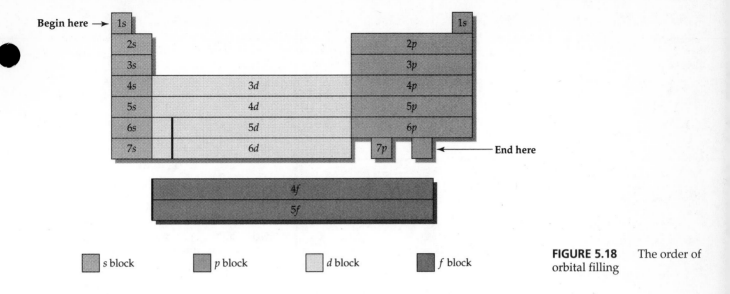

FIGURE 5.18   The order of orbital filling

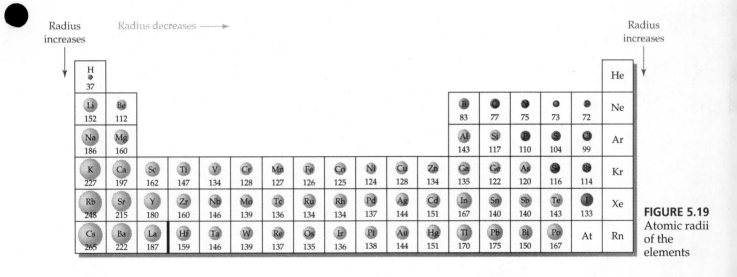

FIGURE 5.19 Atomic radii of the elements

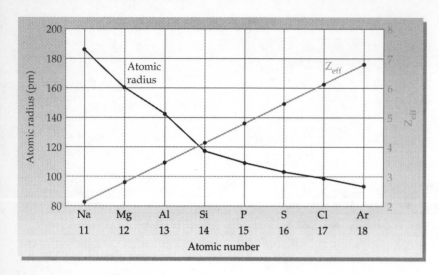

FIGURE 5.20   Plots of Z_{eff} and atomic radius versus atomic number

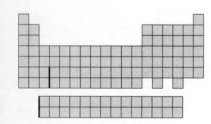

Key Concept Question 5.24   Where on the periodic table do elements that meet the following descriptions appear?

(a) Elements with electrons whose largest principal quantum number is $n = 4$

(b) Elements with the valence-shell ground-state electron configuration $ns^2\,np^3$

(c) Elements that have only one unpaired p electron

(d) The d-block elements

(e) The p-block elements

$r = 215$ pm

$r = 114$ pm

$r = 197$ pm

Key Concept Question 5.28   Which of the following three spheres represents a Ca atom, which an Sr atom, and which a Br atom?

Chapter 6

Ionic Bonds and Some Main-Group Chemistry

TABLE 6.1	Some Common Main-Group Ions and Their Noble Gas Electron Configurations				
Group 1A	**Group 2A**	**Group 3A**	**Group 6A**	**Group 7A**	**Electron Configuration**
H^+					[None]
H^-					[He]
Li^+	Be^{2+}				[He]
Na^+	Mg^{2+}	Al^{3+}	O^{2-}	F^-	[Ne]
K^+	Ca^{2+}	$^*Ga^{3+}$	S^{2-}	Cl^-	[Ar]
Rb^+	Sr^{2+}	$^*In^{3+}$	Se^{2-}	Br^-	[Kr]
Cs^+	Ba^{2+}	$^*Tl^{3+}$	Te^{2-}	I^-	[Xe]

TABLE 6.1 Electron configurations of some main-group ions

*These ions do not have a true noble gas electron configuration because they have an additional filled d subshell.

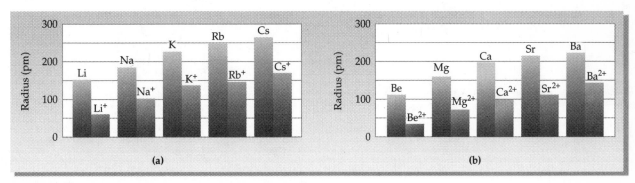

FIGURE 6.1 Radii of group 1A and 2A atoms and their cations

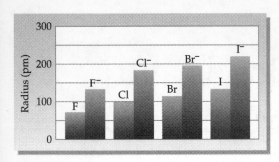

FIGURE 6.2 Radii of group 7A atoms and their anions

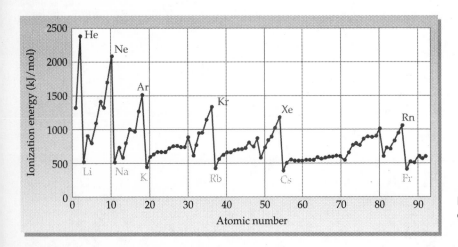

FIGURE 6.3 Ionization energies of the first 92 elements

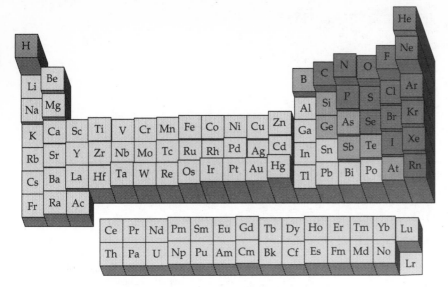

FIGURE 6.4   Ionization energies and the periodic table

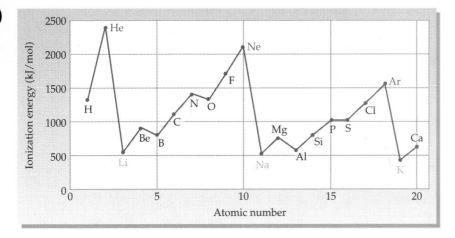

FIGURE 6.5   Ionization energies of the first 20 elements

TABLE 6.2	Higher Ionization Energies (kJ/mol) for Third-Row Elements							
E_i **Number**	**Na**	**Mg**	**Al**	**Si**	**P**	**S**	**Cl**	**Ar**
E_{i1}	496	738	578	787	1,012	1,000	1,251	1,520
E_{i2}	4,562	1,451	1,817	1,577	1,903	2,251	2,297	2,665
E_{i3}	6,912	7,733	2,745	3,231	2,912	3,361	3,822	3,931
E_{i4}	9,543	10,540	11,575	4,356	4,956	4,564	5,158	5,770
E_{i5}	13,353	13,630	14,830	16,091	6,273	7,013	6,540	7,238
E_{i6}	16,610	17,995	18,376	19,784	22,233	8,495	9,458	8,781
E_{i7}	20,114	21,703	23,293	23,783	25,397	27,106	11,020	11,995

TABLE 6.2 Higher ionization energies for third-row elements

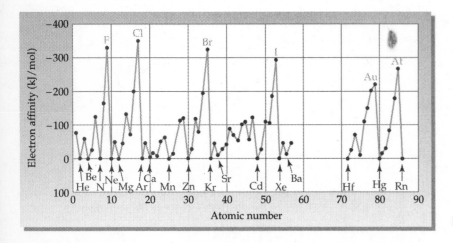

FIGURE 6.6   Electron affinities

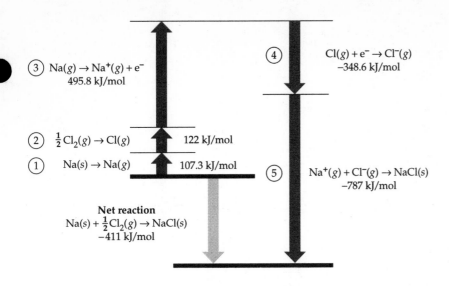

③ $Na(g) \rightarrow Na^+(g) + e^-$
495.8 kJ/mol

④ $Cl(g) + e^- \rightarrow Cl^-(g)$
−348.6 kJ/mol

② $\frac{1}{2}Cl_2(g) \rightarrow Cl(g)$ 122 kJ/mol

① $Na(s) \rightarrow Na(g)$ 107.3 kJ/mol

⑤ $Na^+(g) + Cl^-(g) \rightarrow NaCl(s)$
−787 kJ/mol

Net reaction
$Na(s) + \frac{1}{2}Cl_2(g) \rightarrow NaCl(s)$
−411 kJ/mol

FIGURE 6.8 Born–Haber cycle for the formation of NaCl

TABLE 6.3	Lattice Energies of Some Ionic Solids (kJ/mol)				
	Anion				
Cation	**F⁻**	**Cl⁻**	**Br⁻**	**I⁻**	**O²⁻**
Li^+	1036	853	807	757	2925
Na^+	923	787	747	704	2695
K^+	821	715	682	649	2360
Be^{2+}	3505	3020	2914	2800	4443
Mg^{2+}	2957	2524	2440	2327	3791
Ca^{2+}	2630	2258	2176	2074	3401
Al^{3+}	5215	5492	5361	5218	15,916

TABLE 6.3 Lattice energies of some ionic solids

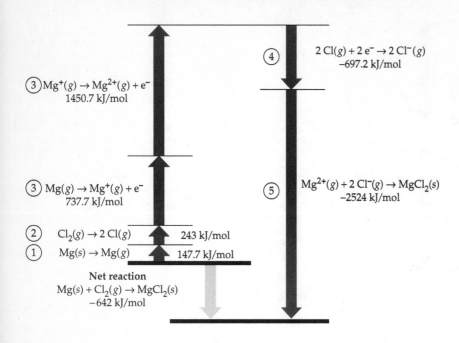

4
2 Cl(g) + 2 e⁻ → 2 Cl⁻(g)
−697.2 kJ/mol
3 Mg⁺(g) → Mg²⁺(g) + e⁻
1450.7 kJ/mol
3 Mg(g) → Mg⁺(g) + e⁻
737.7 kJ/mol
5
Mg²⁺(g) + 2 Cl⁻(g) → MgCl₂(s)
−2524 kJ/mol
2 Cl₂(g) → 2 Cl(g)
243 kJ/mol
1 Mg(s) → Mg(g)
147.7 kJ/mol
Net reaction
Mg(s) + Cl₂(g) → MgCl₂(s)
−642 kJ/mol

FIGURE 6.9 Born–Haber cycle for the formation of $MgCl_2$

1A
8A
H
2A
3A 4A 5A 6A 7A
He
Li Be
B C N O F Ne
Na Mg
3B 4B 5B 6B 7B 8B 1B 2B
Al Si P S Cl Ar
K Ca Sc Ti V Cr Mn Fe Co Ni Cu Zn Ga Ge As Se Br Kr
Rb Sr Y Zr Nb Mo Tc Ru Rh Pd Ag Cd In Sn Sb Te I Xe
Cs Ba La Hf Ta W Re Os Ir Pt Au Hg Tl Pb Bi Po At Rn
Fr Ra Ac Rf Db Sg Bh Hs Mt

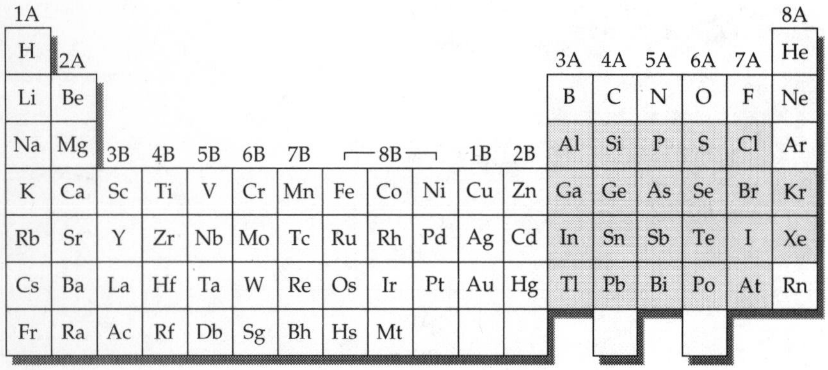

FIGURE 6.10 Failure of the octet rule

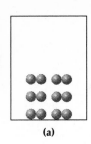   

(a)   (b)   (c)   (d)

Key Concept Question 6.32   Each of the pictures (a)–(d) represents one of the following substances at 25°C: sodium, chlorine, iodine, sodium chloride. Which picture corresponds to which substance?

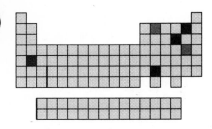

Key Concept Question 6.34   Three binary compounds are represented on the following drawing—red with red, blue with blue, and green with green. Give a likely formula for each compound, and assign oxidation numbers in each.

Chapter 7

Covalent Bonds and Molecular Structure

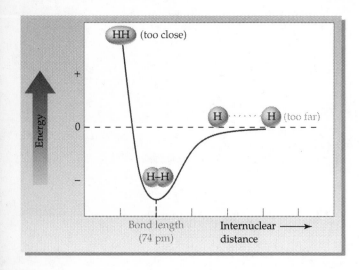

FIGURE 7.2 Potential energy versus distance for the H_2 molecule

TABLE 7.1	Average Bond Dissociation Energies, *D* (kJ/mol)[a]								
H—H	436[a]	C—H	410	N—H	390	O—H	460	F—F	159[a]
H—C	410	C—C	350	N—C	300	O—C	350	Cl—Cl	243[a]
H—F	570[a]	C—F	450	N—F	270	O—F	180	Br—Br	193[a]
H—Cl	432[a]	C—Cl	330	N—Cl	200	O—Cl	200	I—I	151[a]
H—Br	366[a]	C—Br	270	N—Br	240	O—Br	210	S—F	310
H—I	298[a]	C—I	240	N—I	—	O—I	220	S—Cl	250
H—N	390	C—N	300	N—N	240	O—N	200	S—Br	210
H—O	460	C—O	350	N—O	200	O—O	180	S—S	225
H—S	340	C—S	260	N—S	—	O—S	—		

Multiple covalent bonds[b]

C=C	611	C≡C	835	C=O	732	O=O	498[a]	N≡N	945[a]

[a] Exact value
[b] We'll discuss multiple covalent bonds in Section 7.5.

TABLE 7.1 Average bond dissociation energies

Na$^+$ Cl$^-$ An ionic bond

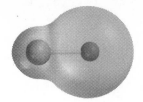

$^{\delta+}$H — Cl$^{\delta-}$

[H :Cl]

   ↑
   └—A polar covalent bond.
The bonding electrons are attracted
more strongly by Cl than by H.

Cl:Cl   A nonpolar covalent bond

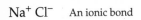

SECTION 7.4   Electrostatic potential maps of NaCl, HCl, and Cl$_2$

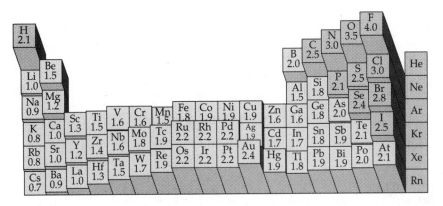

FIGURE 7.4   Electronegativity trends in the periodic table

A CO_2 molecule is linear, with a bond angle of 180°.

An HCN molecule is linear, with a bond angle of 180°.

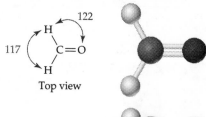

A formaldehyde molecule is trigonal planar, with bond angles of roughly 120°.

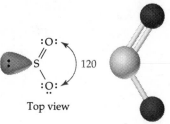

Top view

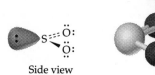

Side view

An SO_2 molecule is bent with a bond angle of approximately 120°.

Top view

Side view

SECTION 7.9 Models of CO_2, HCN, $H_2C=O$, and SO_2

A regular tetrahedron
(a)

(b)

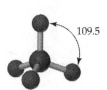

A tetrahedral molecule
(c)

FIGURE 7.5 Tetrahedral geometry

A methane molecule is tetrahedral, with bond angles of 109.5 .

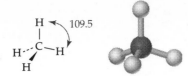

An ammonia molecule is trigonal pyramidal, with bond angles of 107 .

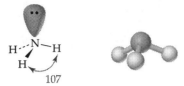

A water molecule is bent, with a bond angle of 104.5 .

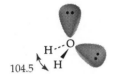

SECTION 7.9   Models of CH_4, NH_3, and H_2O

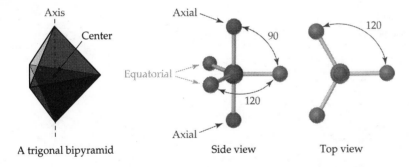

Axis

Center

Equatorial

Axial

Axial

90

120

120

A trigonal bipyramid

Side view

Top view

SECTION 7.9   Trigonal bipyramidal geometry of atoms with five charge clouds

A PCl₅ molecule is trigonal bipyramidal.

An SF₄ molecule is shaped like a seesaw (turn 90° to see it).

A ClF₃ molecule is T-shaped (turn 90° to see it).

An I₃⁻ ion is linear.

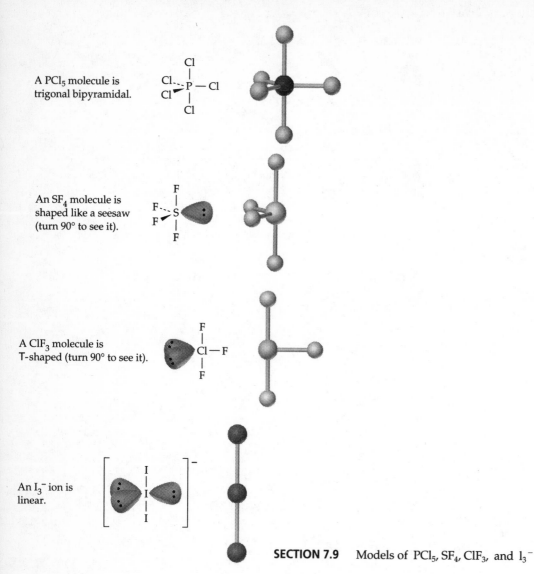

SECTION 7.9 Models of PCl₅, SF₄, ClF₃, and I₃⁻

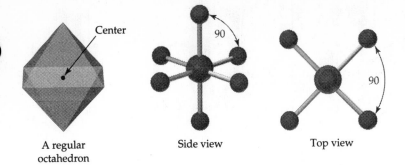

Center

A regular
octahedron

Side view

Top view

90

90

SECTION 7.9   Octahedral geometry of atoms
with six charge clouds

An SF₆ molecule is
octahedral.

An SbCl₅²⁻ ion has a
square pyramidal shape.

An XeF₄ molecule has a
square planar shape.

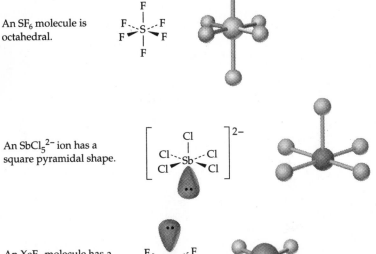

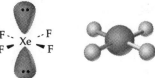

SECTION 7.9   Models of SF_6, $SbCl_5^{2-}$, and XeF_4

TABLE 7.4	Molecular Geometry Around Atoms with 2, 3, 4, 5, and 6 Charge Clouds			
Number of Bonds	**Number of Lone Pairs**	**Number of Charge Clouds**	**Molecular Geometry**	**Example**
2	0	2	Linear	O C O
3	0	3	Trigonal planar	H H C O
2	1		Bent	O O S
4	0	4	Tetrahedral	H H C H H
3	1		Trigonal pyramidal	H N H H
2	2		Bent	H O H

Continued

TABLE 7.4 Molecular geometry

TABLE 7.4   (Continued)

Number of Bonds	Number of Lone Pairs	Number of Charge Clouds	Molecular Geometry	Example
5	0	5	Trigonal bipyramidal	
4	1		Seesaw	
3	2		T-shaped	
2	3		Linear	
6	0	6	Octahedral	
5	1		Square pyramidal	
4	2		Square planar	

TABLE 7.4   Molecular geometry

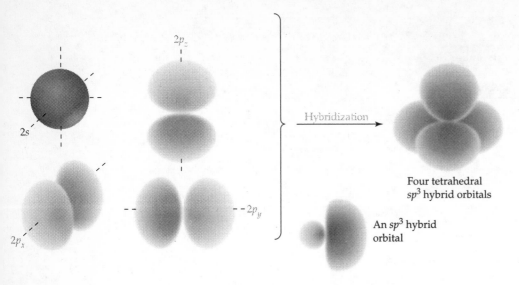

Four tetrahedral sp^3 hybrid orbitals

An sp^3 hybrid orbital

Hybridization

$2p_z$

$2p_y$

$2p_x$

$2s$

FIGURE 7.6 The formation of four sp^3 hybrid orbitals

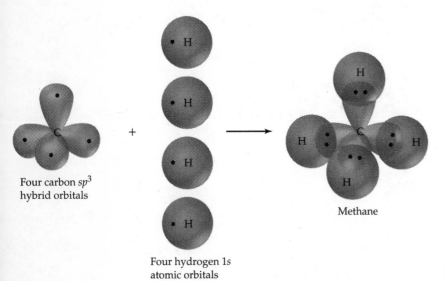

Four carbon sp^3 hybrid orbitals

Four hydrogen $1s$ atomic orbitals

Methane

FIGURE 7.7 The bonding in methane

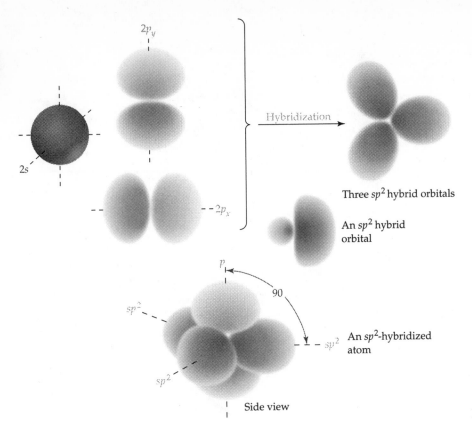

$2p_y$

Hybridization

Three sp^2 hybrid orbitals

An sp^2 hybrid orbital

$2s$

$2p_x$

p

90

sp^2

sp^2

sp^2

sp^2

An sp^2-hybridized atom

Side view

FIGURE 7.8   The formation of sp^2 hybrid orbitals

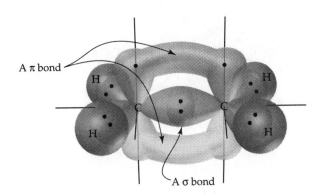

A π bond

H

H

C

C

H

H

A σ bond

FIGURE 7.9   The structure of ethylene

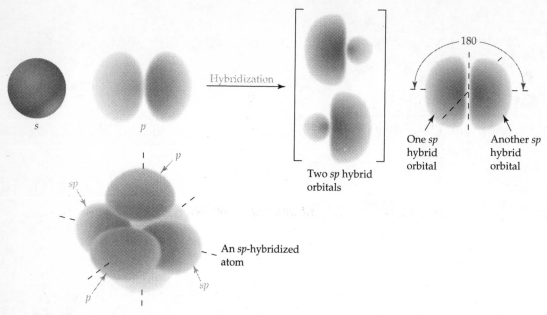

FIGURE 7.10   The formation of *sp* hybrid orbitals

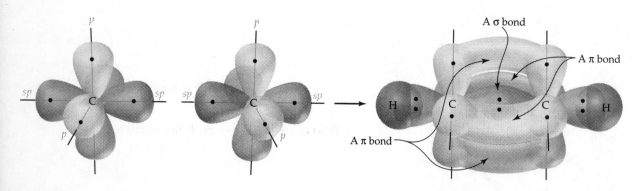

FIGURE 7.11   Formation of a triple bond

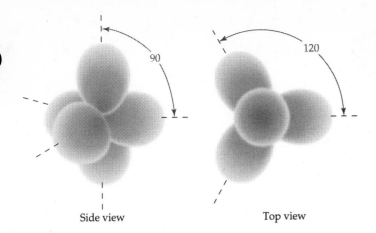

Side view   Top view

FIGURE 7.12   The five sp^3d hybrid orbitals

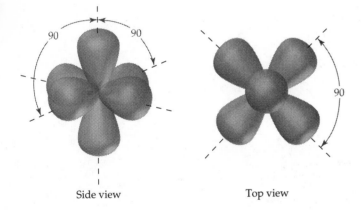

Side view   Top view

FIGURE 7.13   The six sp^3d^2 hybrid orbitals

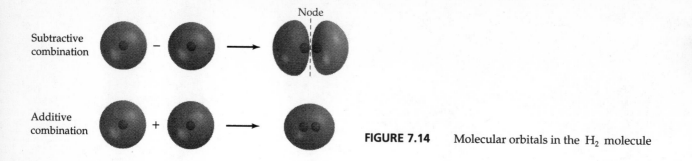

FIGURE 7.14   Molecular orbitals in the H_2 molecule

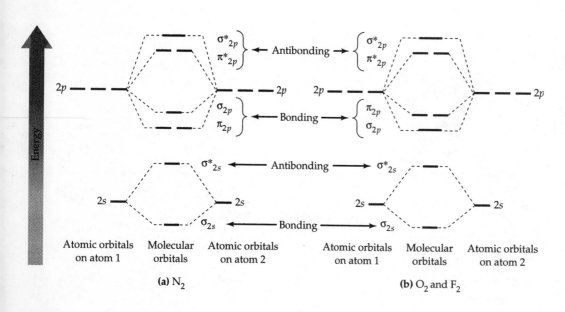

FIGURE 7.18   Molecular orbital energy diagrams for N_2, O_2 and F_2

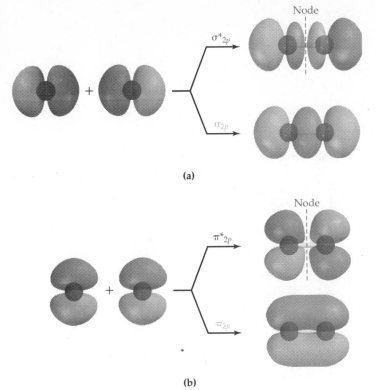

(a)

(b)

FIGURE 7.19   Formation of σ_{2p}, σ^*_{2p}, π_{2p}, and π^*_{2p} MOs

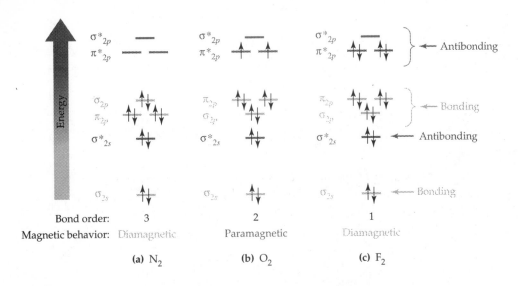

FIGURE 7.20   Molecular orbital diagrams for N_2, O_2, and F_2

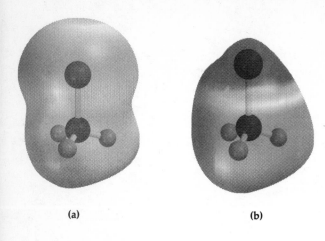

(a)   (b)

Key Concept Question 7.31   Two electrostatic potential maps, one of methyllithium (CH_3Li) and one of chloromethane (CH_3Cl) are shown. Based on their polarity patterns, which do you think is which?

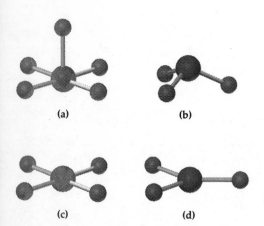

(a)   (b)

(c)   (d)

Key Concept Question 7.32   What is the geometry around the central atom in each of the following molecular models?

Chapter 8

Thermochemistry: Chemical Energy

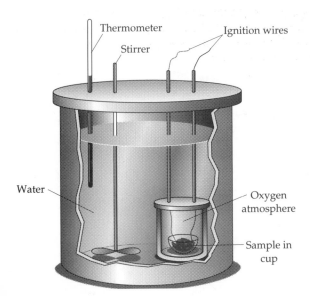

FIGURE 8.9 A bomb calorimeter

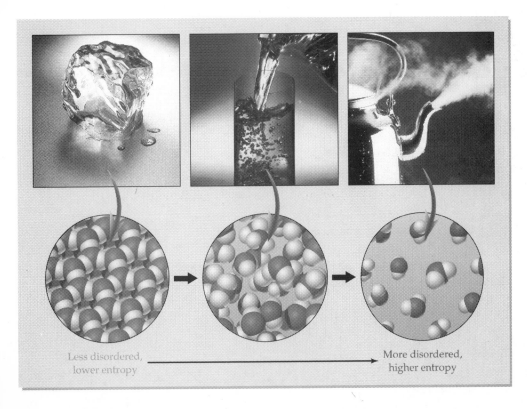

FIGURE 8.13 Entropy and molecular randomness

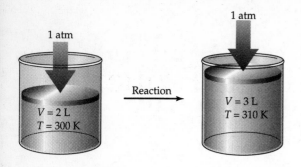

Key Concept Question 8.26 Imagine a reaction that results in a change in both volume and temperature:

  (a) Has any work been done? If so, is its sign positive or negative?

  (b) Has there been an enthalpy change? If so, what is the sign of ΔH? Is the reaction exothermic or endothermic?

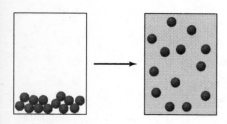

Key Concept Question 8.32 What are the signs of ΔH, ΔS, and ΔG for the following spontaneous change? Explain.

Chapter 9

Gases: Their Properties and Behavior

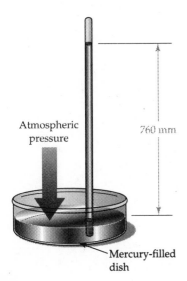

Atmospheric pressure

760 mm

Mercury-filled dish

FIGURE 9.3 A mercury barometer

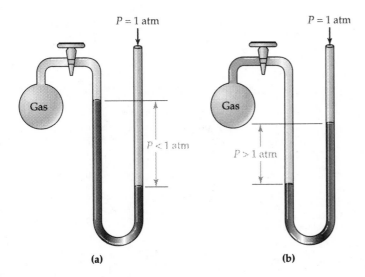

$P = 1$ atm

Gas

$P < 1$ atm

(a)

$P = 1$ atm

Gas

$P > 1$ atm

(b)

FIGURE 9.4 Open-end manometers

TABLE 9.2 Pressure–Volume Measurements on a Gas Sample	
Pressure (mm Hg)	**Volume (L)**
760	1
380	2
253	3
190	4
152	5
127	6
109	7
95	8
84	9
76	10

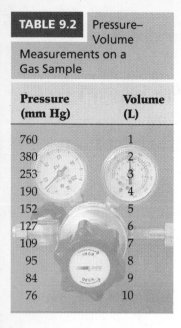

TABLE 9.2 Pressure–volume measurements and Boyle's law

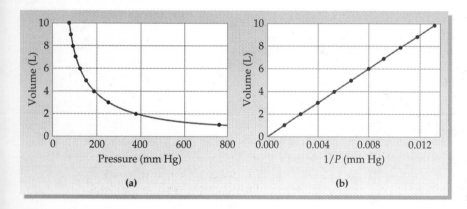

(a) (b)

FIGURE 9.6 Pressure–volume measurements and Boyle's law

TABLE 9.3 Temperature–Volume Measurements on a Gas Sample at Constant n, P	
Temperature (K)	**Volume (L)**
123	0.45
173	0.63
223	0.82
273	1.00
323	1.18
373	1.37

TABLE 9.3   Temperature–volume measurements and Charles' law

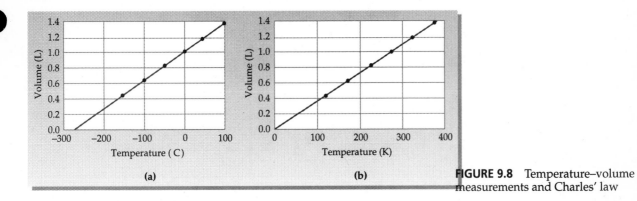

(a)   (b)

FIGURE 9.8   Temperature–volume measurements and Charles' law

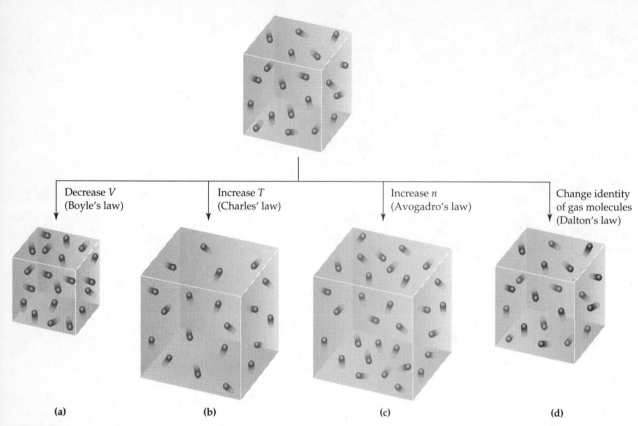

Decrease V
(Boyle's law)

Increase T
(Charles' law)

Increase n
(Avogadro's law)

Change identity
of gas molecules
(Dalton's law)

(a)   (b)   (c)   (d)

FIGURE 9.11 Kinetic–molecular theory and the gas laws

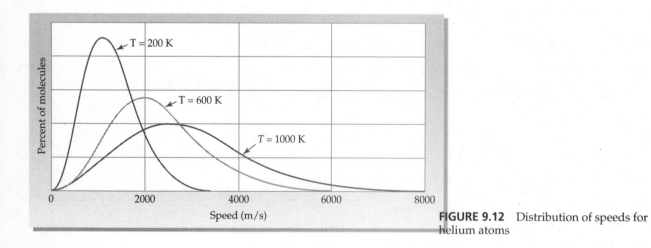

FIGURE 9.12 Distribution of speeds for helium atoms

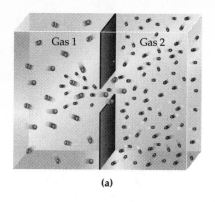

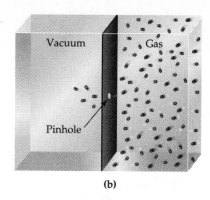

(a)   (b)

FIGURE 9.13   Diffusion and effusion

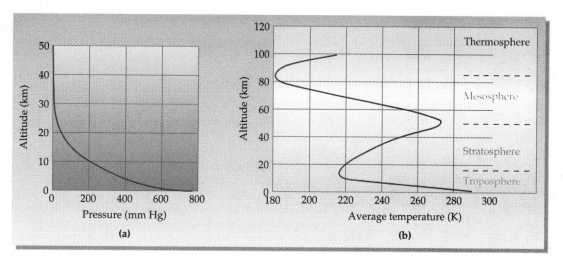

(a)   (b)

FIGURE 9.16   Variations of pressure and temperature with altitude

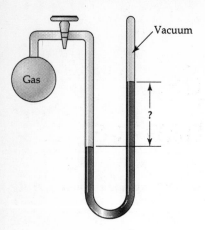

Key Concept Question 9.30 The apparatus shown is called a *closed-end* manometer because the arm not connected to the gas sample is closed to the atmosphere and is under vacuum. Explain how you can read the gas pressure in the bulb.

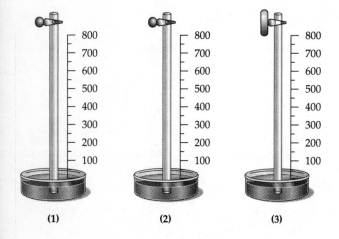

Key Concept Question 9.33 A glass tube has one end in a dish of mercury and the other end closed by a stopcock. The distance from the surface of the mercury to the bottom of the stopcock is 800 mm. The apparatus is at 25°C, and the mercury level in the tube is the same as that in the dish.

Chapter 10

Liquids, Solids, and Phase Changes

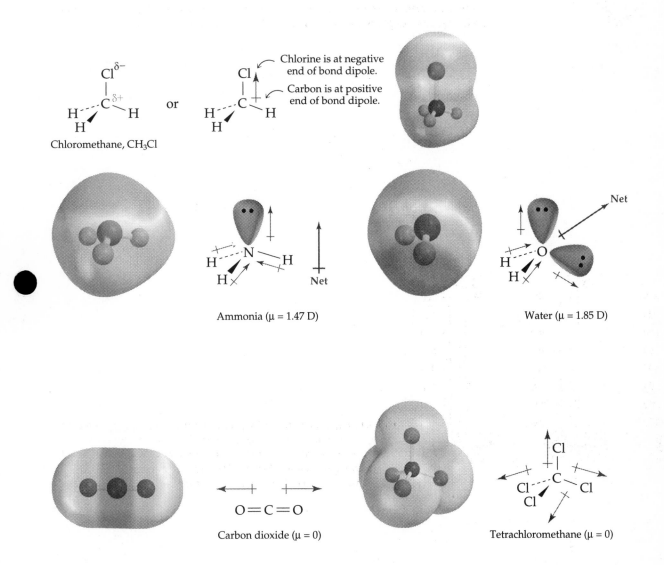

Chloromethane, CH₃Cl

Chlorine is at negative end of bond dipole.

Carbon is at positive end of bond dipole.

Ammonia (μ = 1.47 D)

Water (μ = 1.85 D)

Carbon dioxide (μ = 0)

O=C=O

Tetrachloromethane (μ = 0)

SECTION 10.1 Electrostatic potential maps of CH₃Cl, NH₃, H₂O, CO₂, and CCl₄

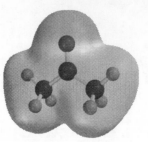

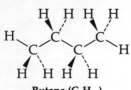

Butane (C₄H₁₀)

Mol mass = 58 amu
bp = −0.5°C

Acetone (C₃H₆O)

Mol mass = 58 amu
bp = 56.2°C

SECTION 10.2 Electrostatic potential maps of butane and acetone

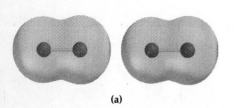

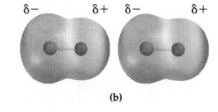

(a)

(b)

FIGURE 10.5 Origin of London dispersion forces

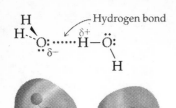

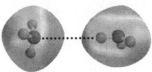

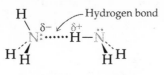

SECTION 10.2   Electrostatic potential maps of hydrogen bonds in H_2O and NH_3

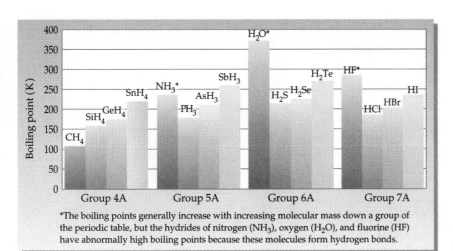

*The boiling points generally increase with increasing molecular mass down a group of the periodic table, but the hydrides of nitrogen (NH_3), oxygen (H_2O), and fluorine (HF) have abnormally high boiling points because these molecules form hydrogen bonds.

TABLE 10.4   Boiling points of covalent binary hydrides

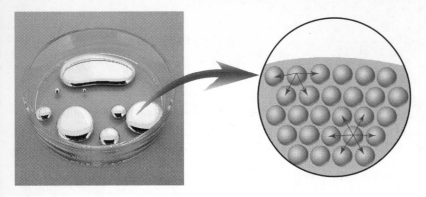

FIGURE 10.8   Surface tension

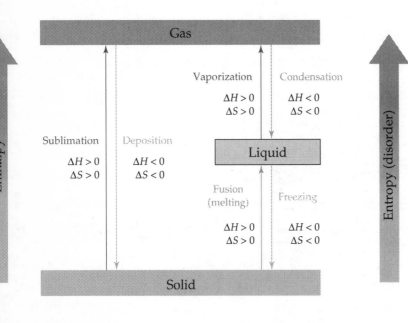

FIGURE 10.9 ΔS and ΔH for phase changes

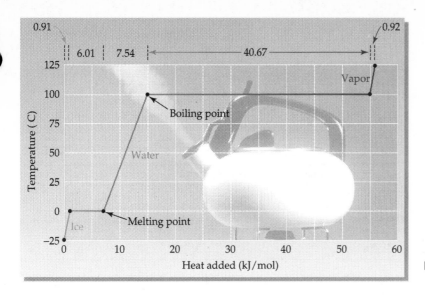

FIGURE 10.10   Heating curve for H_2O

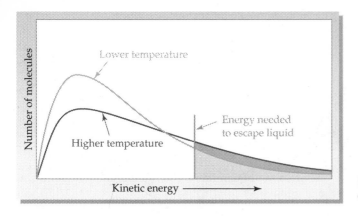

FIGURE 10.12   The distribution of molecular kinetic energies in a liquid

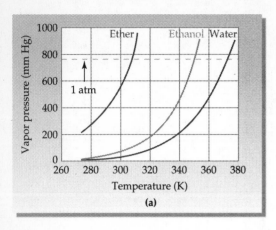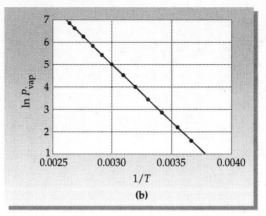

FIGURE 10.13   Vapor pressures of water, ethanol, and diethyl ether

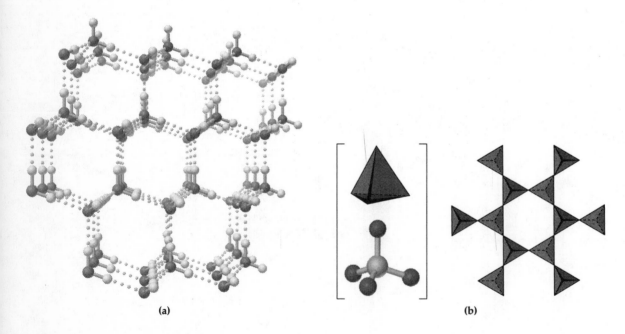

FIGURE 10.15   Crystal structures of ice and quartz

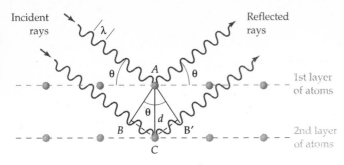

Incident rays | Reflected rays

λ

θ   A   θ

1st layer of atoms

θ   d

B   B′

2nd layer of atoms

C

FIGURE 10.18   Diffraction of X rays from atoms in the top two layers of a crystal

Simple cubic
(a)

Body-centered cubic
(b)

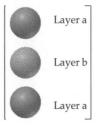

Layer a

Layer b

Layer a

FIGURE 10.20   Simple cubic packing and body-centered cubic packing

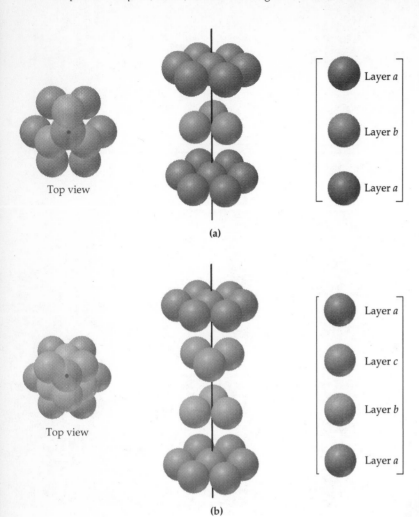

Top view

(a)

Layer *a*
Layer *b*
Layer *a*

Top view

(b)

Layer *a*
Layer *c*
Layer *b*
Layer *a*

FIGURE 10.21 Hexagonal closest-packing and cubic closest-packing

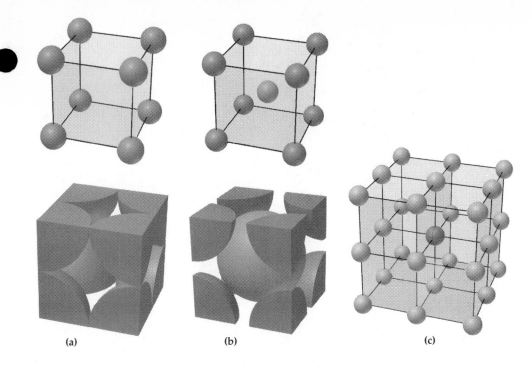

(a)   (b)   (c)

FIGURE 10.22   Primitive-cubic and body-centered cubic unit cells

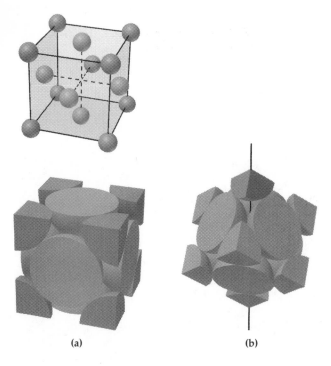

(a)   (b)

FIGURE 10.23   A face-centered cubic unit cell

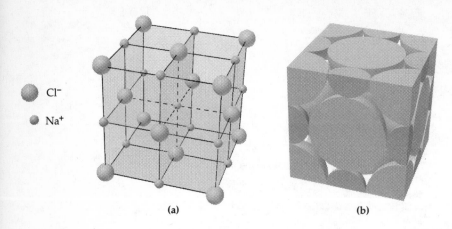

Cl⁻

Na⁺

(a)

(b)

FIGURE 10.24   The unit cell of NaCl

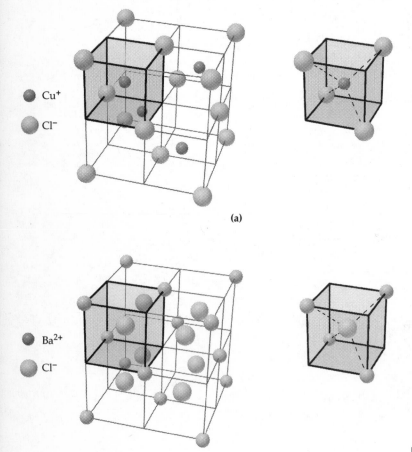

Cu⁺

Cl⁻

(a)

Ba²⁺

Cl⁻

(b)

FIGURE 10.25   Unit cells of CuCl and BaCl$_2$

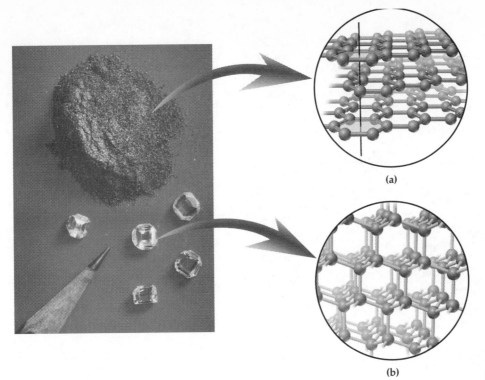

FIGURE 10.26 Structures of graphite and diamond

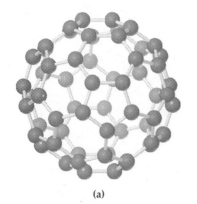

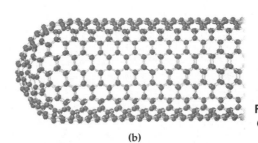

FIGURE 10.27 Structure of fullerene, C_{60}, and carbon nanotubes

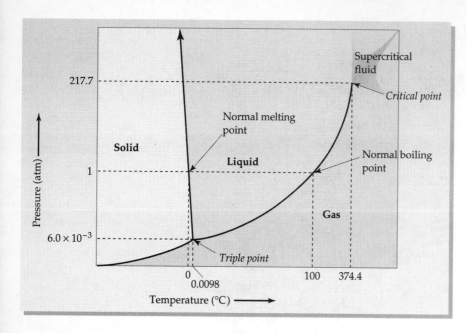

FIGURE 10.28 Phase diagram for H_2O

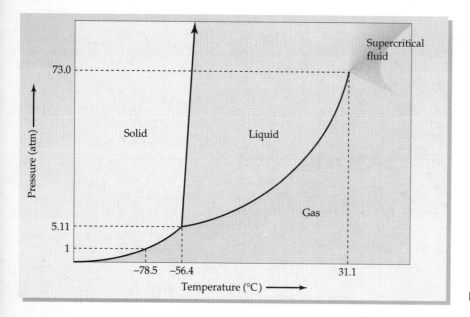

FIGURE 10.29 Phase diagram for CO_2

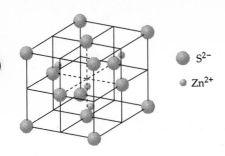

● S^{2-}

● Zn^{2+}

Key Concept Question 10.24   Zinc sulfide, or sphalerite, crystallizes in the following cubic unit cell:

(a) What kind of packing do the sulfide ions adopt?

(b) How many S^{2-} ions and how many Zn^{2+} ions are in the unit cell?

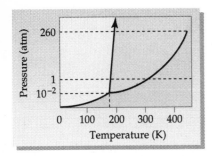

Key Concept Question 10.26   The phase diagram of a substance is shown below.

(a) Approximately what is the normal boiling point, and what is the normal melting point of the substance?

(b) What is the physical state of the substance under the following conditions?

(i) $T = 150$ K, $P = 0.5$ atm

(ii) $T = 325$ K, $P = 0.9$ atm

(iii) $T = 450$ K, $P = 265$ atm

Chapter 11

Solutions and Their Properties

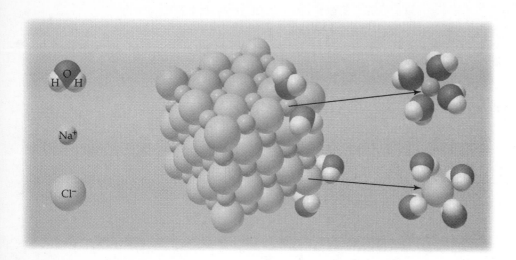

FIGURE 11.1 Dissolution of an NaCl crystal in water

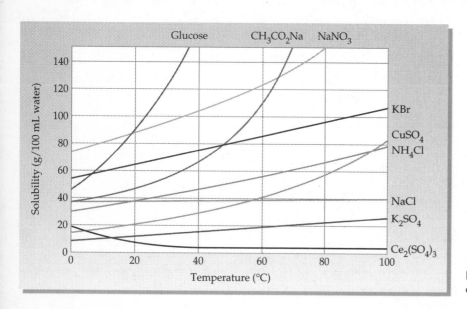

FIGURE 11.6 Solubilities of some common solids in water

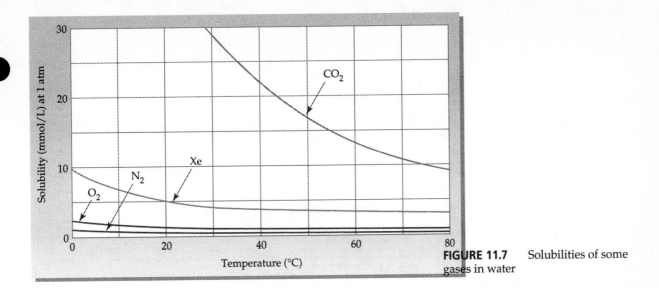

FIGURE 11.7 Solubilities of some gases in water

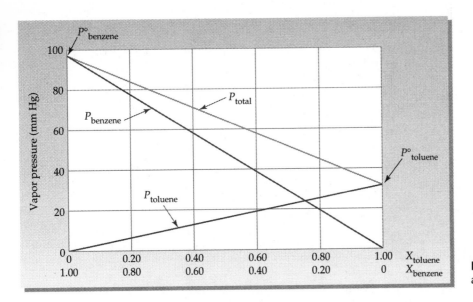

FIGURE 11.11 The vapor pressure of a solution of benzene and toluene

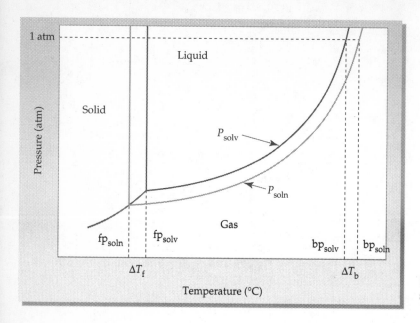

FIGURE 11.12 Phase diagrams for a pure solvent and a solution

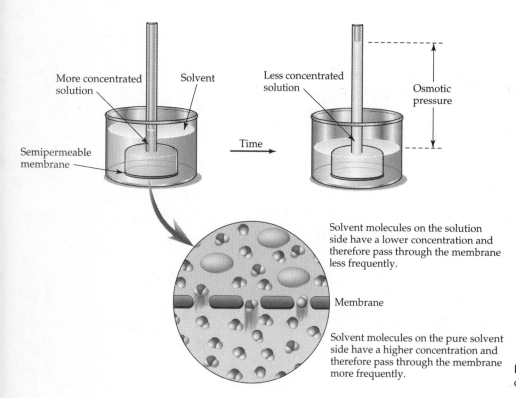

Solvent molecules on the solution side have a lower concentration and therefore pass through the membrane less frequently.

Membrane

Solvent molecules on the pure solvent side have a higher concentration and therefore pass through the membrane more frequently.

FIGURE 11.15 The phenomenon of osmosis

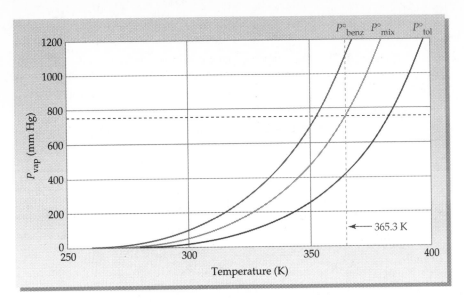

FIGURE 11.17   Vapor-pressure curves for benzene, toluene, and a 1:1 mixture

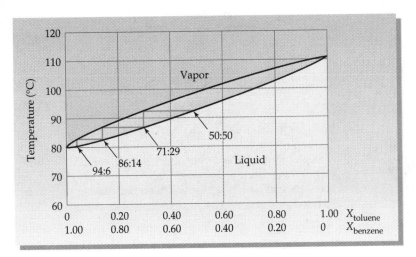

FIGURE 11.18   Phase diagram of temperature versus composition

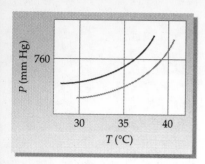

Key Concept Question 11.29 The following phase diagram shows part of the liquid/vapor phase-transition boundaries for pure ether and a solution of a non-volatile solute in ether.

(a) What is the approximate normal boiling point of pure ether?

(b) What is the approximate molal concentration of the solute? [K_b for ether is 2.02 (°C · kg)/mol.]

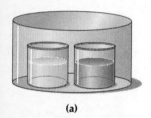

(a)

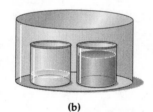

(b)

Key Concept Question 11.34 Two beakers, one with pure water (blue) and the other with a solution of NaCl in water (green), are placed in a closed container as represented by drawing (a). Which of the drawings (b)–(d) represents what the beakers will look like after a substantial amount of time has passed?

Chapter 12

Chemical Kinetics

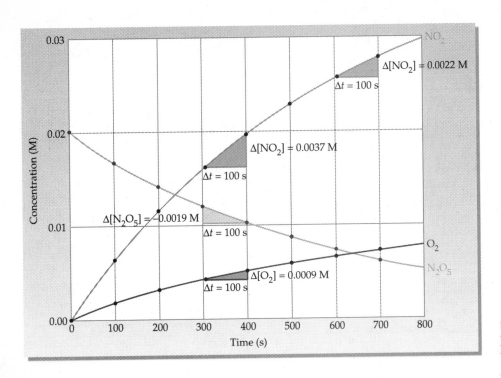

FIGURE 12.1 Concentration versus time plots for the decomposition of N_2O_5

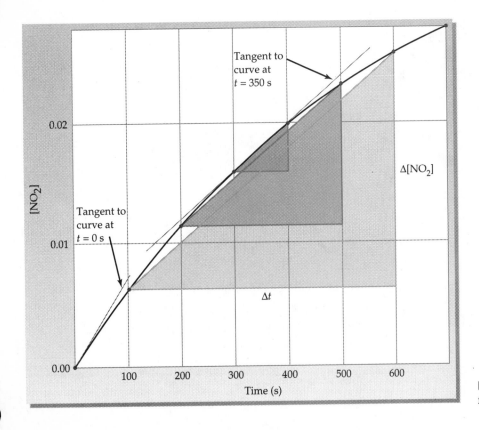

FIGURE 12.2 Rate of NO_2 formation from a concentration–time plot

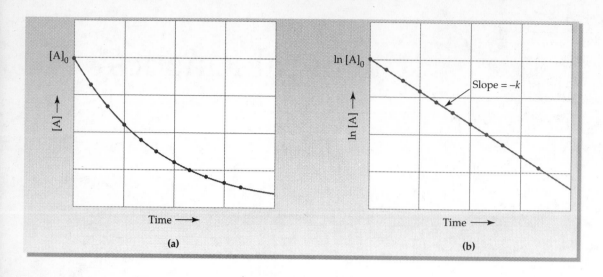

FIGURE 12.6 Reactant concentration versus time for a first-order reaction

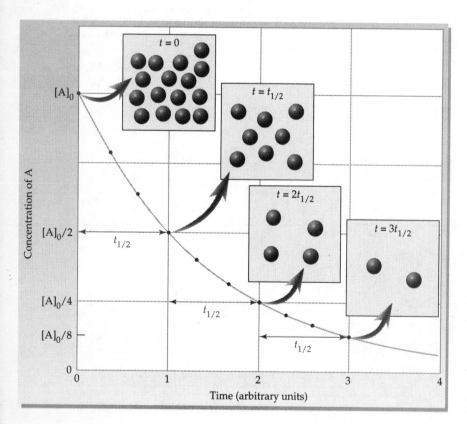

FIGURE 12.7 Half-life of a first-order reaction

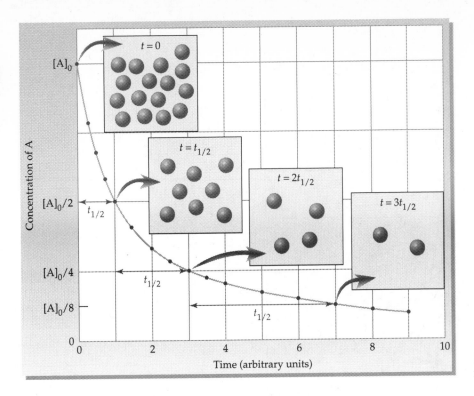

FIGURE 12.8   Half-life of a second-order reaction

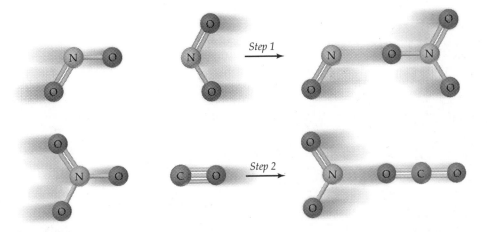

FIGURE 12.10   Elementary steps in the reaction of NO_2 with CO_2

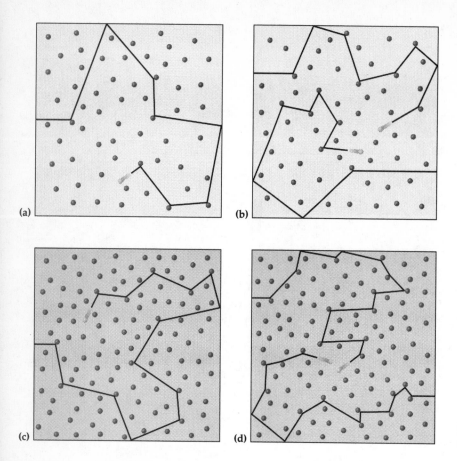

FIGURE 12.11 Effect of concentration on collision frequency

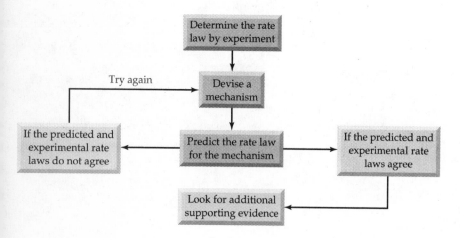

FIGURE 12.12 Logic used in studies of reaction mechanisms

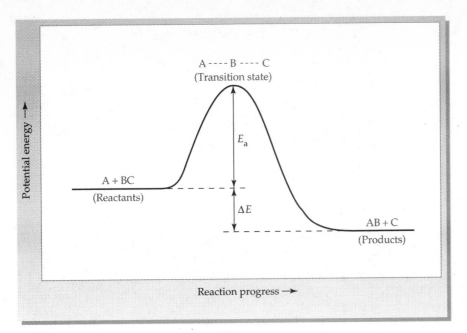

FIGURE 12.14 Potential energy profile for a chemical reaction

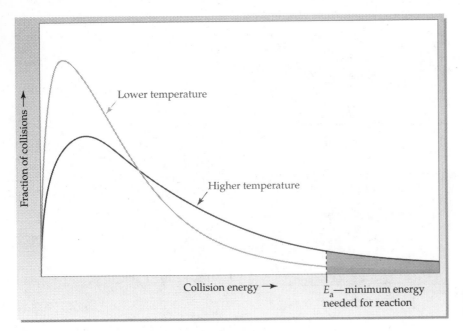

FIGURE 12.15 Distribution of collision energies

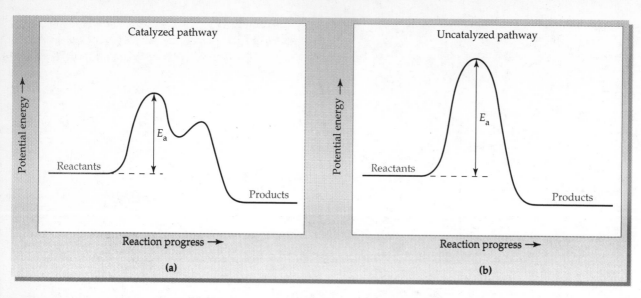

FIGURE 12.17 Potential energy profiles for a reaction, catalyzed and uncatalyzed

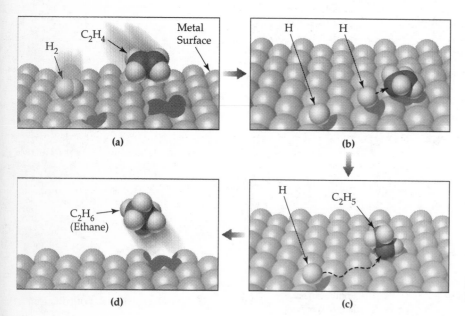

FIGURE 12.18 Catalytic hydrogenation of ethylene

  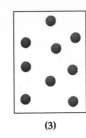

(1)   **(2)**   **(3)**

Key Concept Question 12.23   Consider the first-order decomposition of A molecules (red spheres) in three vessels of equal volume.

(a) What are the relative rates of decomposition in vessels (1)–(3)?

(b) What are the relative half-lives of the reactions in vessels (1)–(3)?

(c) How will the rates and half-lives be affected if the volume of each vessel is decreased by a factor of 2?

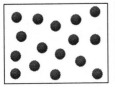

$t = 0$ min $t = 1$ min

$t = 3$ min $t = ?$ min

Key Concept Question 12.26   The following pictures represent the progress of a reaction in which two A molecules combine to give a more complex molecule A_2, $2A \rightarrow A_2$.

(a) Is the reaction first order or second order in A?

(b) What is the rate law?

(c) Draw an appropriate picture in the last box, and specify the time.

Chapter 13 Chemical Equilibrium

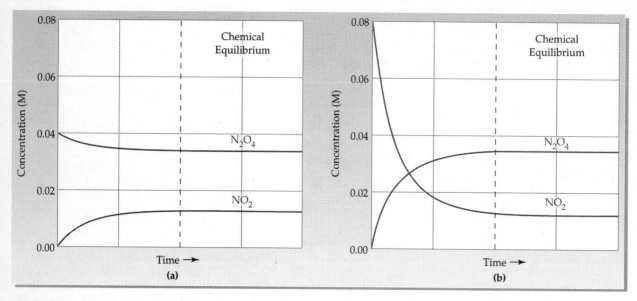

FIGURE 13.1   Change in concentrations for the decomposition of N_2O_4 to NO_2

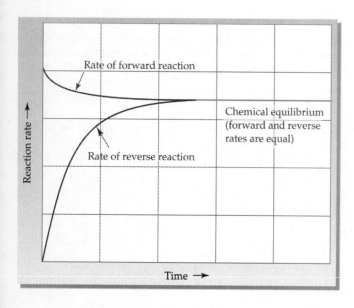

FIGURE 13.2   Forward and reverse reaction rates for the decomposition of N_2O_4 to NO_2

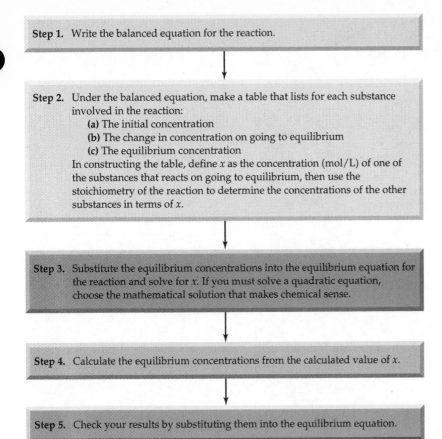

Step 1. Write the balanced equation for the reaction.

Step 2. Under the balanced equation, make a table that lists for each substance involved in the reaction:
    (a) The initial concentration
    (b) The change in concentration on going to equilibrium
    (c) The equilibrium concentration
In constructing the table, define x as the concentration (mol/L) of one of the substances that reacts on going to equilibrium, then use the stoichiometry of the reaction to determine the concentrations of the other substances in terms of x.

Step 3. Substitute the equilibrium concentrations into the equilibrium equation for the reaction and solve for x. If you must solve a quadratic equation, choose the mathematical solution that makes chemical sense.

Step 4. Calculate the equilibrium concentrations from the calculated value of x.

Step 5. Check your results by substituting them into the equilibrium equation.

FIGURE 13.6 Steps in calculating equilibrium concentrations from initial concentrations

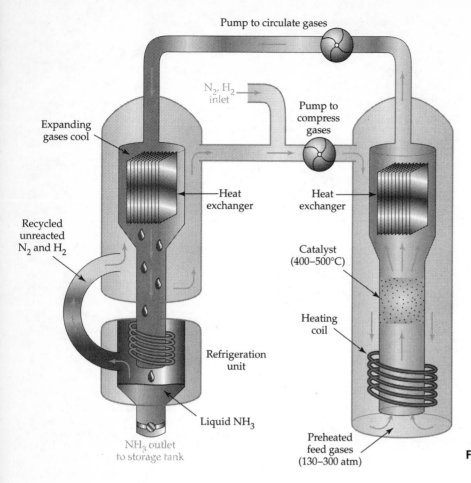

Pump to circulate gases

N₂, H₂ inlet

Pump to compress gases

Expanding gases cool

Heat exchanger

Heat exchanger

Catalyst (400–500°C)

Recycled unreacted N₂ and H₂

Heating coil

Refrigeration unit

Liquid NH₃

NH₃ outlet to storage tank

Preheated feed gases (130–300 atm)

FIGURE 13.7 Haber process for ammonia

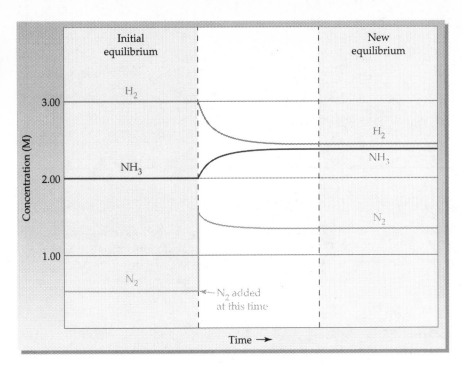

FIGURE 13.8   Changes in concentration when an equilibrium is disturbed

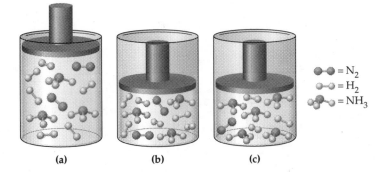

FIGURE 13.11   Effect of pressure and volume on an equilibrium

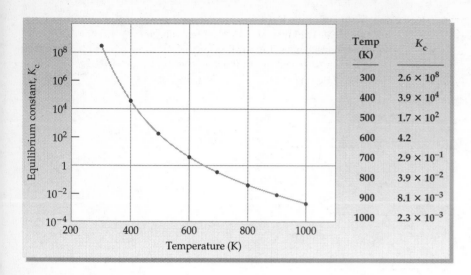

Temp (K)	K_c
300	2.6×10^8
400	3.9×10^4
500	1.7×10^2
600	4.2
700	2.9×10^{-1}
800	3.9×10^{-2}
900	8.1×10^{-3}
1000	2.3×10^{-3}

FIGURE 13.12 Effect of temperature on the equilibrium for conversion of N_2 and H_2 to NH_3

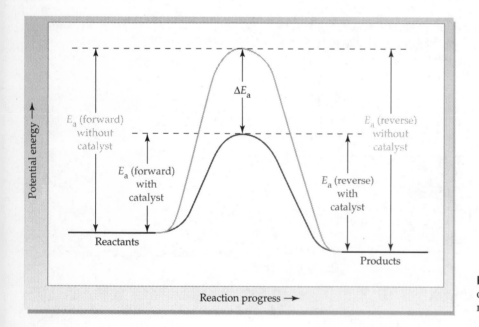

FIGURE 13.14 Effect of a catalyst on the potential energy profile for a reaction

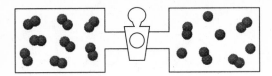

Key Concept Question 13.32 Consider the reaction $A + B \rightleftharpoons AB$. The vessel on the right contains an equilibrium mixture of A molecules (red spheres), B molecules (blue spheres), and AB molecules. If the stopcock is opened and the contents of the two vessels are allowed to mix, will the reaction go in the forward or reverse direction? Explain.

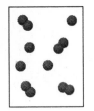

$T = 325\ K$ $T = 350\ K$

Key Concept Question 13.34 The following pictures represent equilibrium mixtures at 325 K and 350 K for a reaction involving A atoms (red), B atoms (blue), and AB molecules:

(a) Write a balanced equation for the reaction that occurs on raising the temperature.

(b) Is the reaction exothermic or endothermic? Explain using Le Châtelier's principle.

(c) If the volume of the container is increased, will the number of A atoms increase, decrease, or remain the same? Explain.

Chapter 14

Hydrogen, Oxygen, and Water

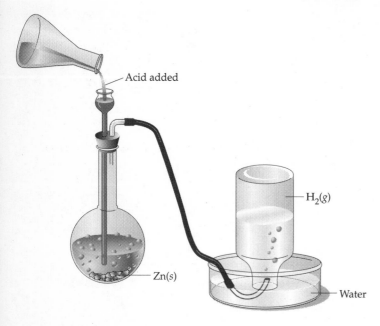

Acid added

H$_2$(g)

Zn(s)

Water

FIGURE 14.1 Generating and collecting hydrogen

TABLE 14.1	Properties of Hydrogen Isotopes		
Property	**Protium**	**Deuterium**	**Tritium**
Atomic hydrogen (H)			
Mass, amu	1.0078	2.0141	3.0160
Ionization energy, kJ/mol	1311.7	1312.2	
Nuclear stability	Stable	Stable	Radioactive
Molecular hydrogen (H_2)			
Melting point, K	13.96	18.73	20.62
Boiling point, K	20.39	23.67	25.04
Bond dissociation energy, kJ/mol	435.9	443.4	446.9
Water (H_2O)			
Melting point, °C	0.00	3.81	4.48
Boiling point, °C	100.00	101.42	101.51
Density at 25°C, g/mL	0.997	1.104	1.214
Dissociation constant at 25°C	1.01×10^{-14}	0.195×10^{-14}	$\sim 0.06 \times 10^{-14}$

TABLE 14.1 Properties of hydrogen isotopes

1 1A	2 2A			13 3A	14 4A	15 5A	16 6A	17 7A	18 8A
LiH 692	BeH$_2$ d 250			B$_2$H$_6$ −165	CH$_4$ −182	NH$_3$ −78	H$_2$O 0	HF −83	
NaH d 800	MgH$_2$ d 280			AlH$_3$ d 150	SiH$_4$ −185	PH$_3$ −134	H$_2$S −86	HCl −115	
KH d	CaH$_2$ 816			GaH$_3$ −15	GeH$_4$ −165	AsH$_3$ −116	H$_2$Se −66	HBr −88	
RbH d	SrH$_2$ d 675			InH$_3$ (?)	SnH$_4$ −146	SbH$_3$ −88	H$_2$Te −51	HI −51	
CsH d	BaH$_2$ d 675			TlH$_3$ (?)	PbH$_4$	BiH$_3$	H$_2$Po	HAt	

FIGURE 14.2   Binary hydrides of main-group elements

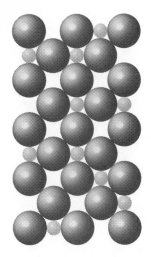

FIGURE 14.3   Structure of an interstitial metallic hydride

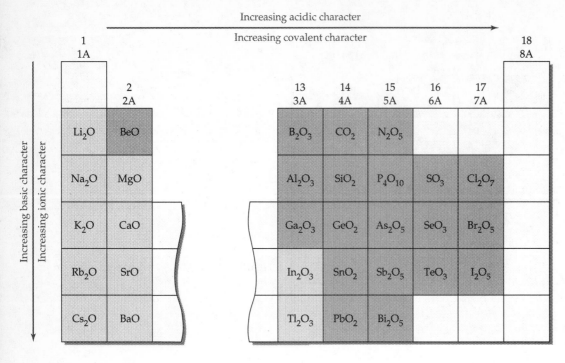

FIGURE 14.6 Basic, acidic, and amphoteric oxides of main-group elements

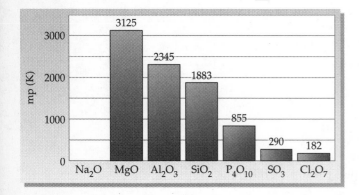

FIGURE 14.7   Melting points of oxides (kelvins)

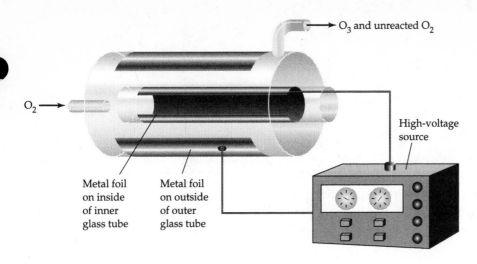

→ O₃ and unreacted O₂

O₂ →

High-voltage
source

Metal foil
on inside
of inner
glass tube

Metal foil
on outside
of outer
glass tube

FIGURE 14.10 Generator for preparing ozone

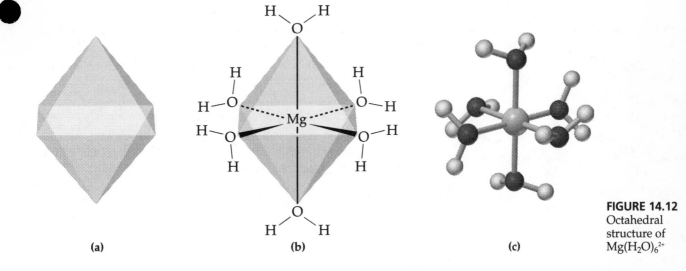

(a)

(b)

(c)

FIGURE 14.12
Octahedral
structure of
$Mg(H_2O)_6{}^{2+}$

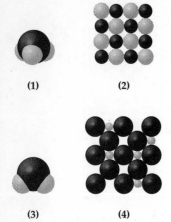

(1)   **(2)**

(3)   **(4)**

Key Concept Question 14.20 In the following pictures of binary hydrides, ivory spheres represent H atoms or ions, and burgundy spheres represent atoms or ions of the other element.

(a) Identify each binary hydride as ionic, covalent, or interstitial.

(b) What is the oxidation state of hydrogen in compounds (1), (2), and (3)? What is the oxidation state of the other element?

Key Concept Question 14.24 In the following pictures of oxides, red spheres represent O atoms or ions, and green spheres represent atoms or ions of a first- or second-row element in its highest oxidation state.

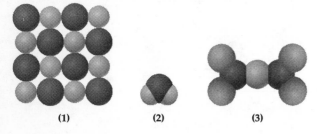

(1)   **(2)**   **(3)**

(a) What is the oxidation state of oxygen in each oxide? What is the oxidation state of the other element?

(b) Which of these oxides is (are) molecular, and which has (have) an infinitely extended three-dimensional structure?

(c) Which of these oxides is (are) likely to be a gas or a liquid, and which is (are) likely to be a high-melting solid?

(d) Identify the other element in (2) and (3).

Chapter 15

Aqueous Equilibria: Acids and Bases

TABLE 15.1	Relative Strengths of Conjugate Acid–Base Pairs			
	Acid, HA		**Base, A⁻**	

Stronger acid

$HClO_4$
HCl
H_2SO_4
HNO_3

Strong acids. 100% dissociated in aqueous solution.

H_3O^+

HSO_4^-
H_3PO_4
HNO_2
HF
CH_3CO_2H
H_2CO_3
H_2S
NH_4^+
HCN
HCO_3^-

Weak acids. Exist in solution as a mixture of HA, A^-, and H_3O^+.

H_2O

NH_3
OH^-
H_2

Very weak acids Negligible tendency to dissociate.

Weaker acid

ClO_4^-
Cl^-
HSO_4^-
NO_3^-

Very weak bases. Negligible tendency to be protonated in aqueous solution.

H_2O

SO_4^{2-}
$H_2PO_4^-$
NO_2^-
F^-
$CH_3CO_2^-$
HCO_3^-
HS^-
NH_3
CN^-
CO_3^{2-}

Weak bases. Moderate tendency to be protonated in aqueous solution.

OH^-

NH_2^-
O^{2-}
H^-

Strong bases. 100% protonated in aqueous solution.

Weaker base

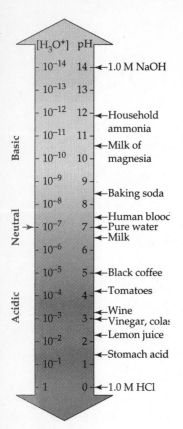

FIGURE 15.3   The pH scale and pH values for some common substances

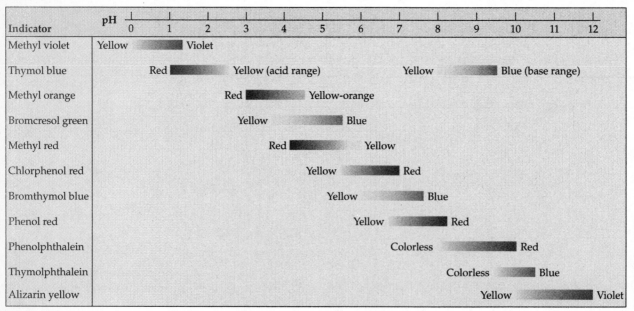

FIGURE 15.4 Acid–base indicators and their color changes

TABLE 15.2   Acid–Dissociation Constants at 25°C

	Acid	Molecular Formula	Structural Formula*	K_a	$pK_a^\dagger$
Stronger acid	Hydrochloric	HCl	H—Cl	2×10^6	−6.3
	Nitrous	HNO_2	H—O—N=O	4.5×10^{-4}	3.35
	Hydrofluoric	HF	H—F	3.5×10^{-4}	3.46
	Acetylsalicylic (aspirin)	$C_9H_8O_4$		3.0×10^{-4}	3.52
	Formic	HCO_2H		1.8×10^{-4}	3.74
	Ascorbic (vitamin C)	$C_6H_8O_6$		8.0×10^{-5}	4.10
	Benzoic	$C_6H_5CO_2H$		6.5×10^{-5}	4.19
	Acetic	CH_3CO_2H		1.8×10^{-5}	4.74
	Hypochlorous	HOCl	H—O—Cl	3.5×10^{-8}	7.46
	Hydrocyanic	HCN	H—C≡N	4.9×10^{-10}	9.31
Weaker acid	Methanol	CH_3OH	CH_3—O—H	2.9×10^{-16}	15.54

* The proton that is transferred to water when the acid dissociates is shown in color. $^\dagger pK_a = -\log K_a$.

Step 1. List the species present before dissociation and identify them as Brønsted–Lowry acids or bases.

Step 2. Write balanced equations for all possible proton-transfer reactions.

Step 3. Identify the principal reaction—the reaction that has the largest equilibrium constant.

Step 4. Make a table that lists the following values for each of the species involved in the principal reaction:
    (a) The initial concentration
    (b) The change in concentration on proceeding to equilibrium
    (c) The equilibrium concentration
In constructing this table, define x as the concentration (mol/L) of the acid that dissociates.

Step 5. Substitute the equilibrium concentrations into the equilibrium equation for the principal reaction, and solve for x.

Step 6. Calculate the "big" concentrations—the concentrations of the species involved in the principal reaction.

Step 7. Use the big concentrations and the equilibrium equations for the subsidiary reactions to calculate the small concentrations—the concentrations of the species involved in the subsidiary equilibria.

Step 8. Calculate the pH $= -\log[H_3O^+]$.

FIGURE 15.7 Steps in solving weak acid problems

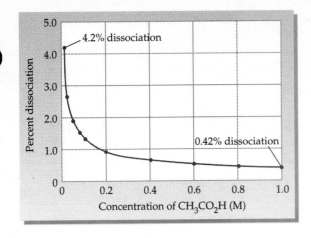

FIGURE 15.8 Percent dissociation of a weak acid

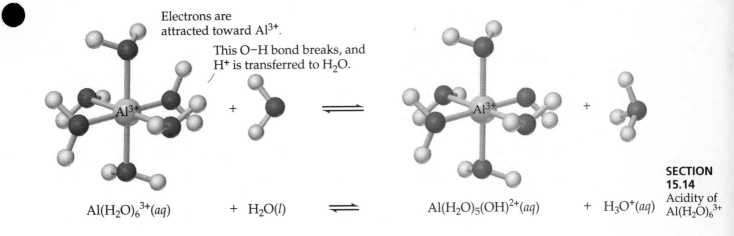

Electrons are attracted toward Al^{3+}.

This O–H bond breaks, and H^+ is transferred to H_2O.

$$Al(H_2O)_6^{3+}(aq) \quad + \quad H_2O(l) \quad \rightleftharpoons \quad Al(H_2O)_5(OH)^{2+}(aq) \quad + \quad H_3O^+(aq)$$

**SECTION
15.14**
Acidity of
$Al(H_2O)_6^{3+}$

TABLE 15.5 Acid–Base Properties of Salts

Type of Salt	Examples	Ions That React with Water	pH of Solution
Cation from strong base; anion from strong acid	$NaCl$, KNO_3, BaI_2	None	~ 7
Cation from weak base; anion from strong acid	NH_4Cl, NH_4NO_3, $[(CH_3)_3NH]Cl$	Cation	< 7
Small, highly charged cation; anion from strong acid	$AlCl_3$, $Cr(NO_3)_3$, $Fe(ClO_4)_3$	Hydrated cation	< 7
Cation from strong base; anion from weak acid	$NaCN$, KF, Na_2CO_3	Anion	> 7
Cation from weak base; anion from weak acid	NH_4CN, NH_4F, $(NH_4)_2CO_3$	Cation and anion	< 7 if $K_a > K_b$ > 7 if $K_a < K_b$ ~ 7 if $K_a \approx K_b$

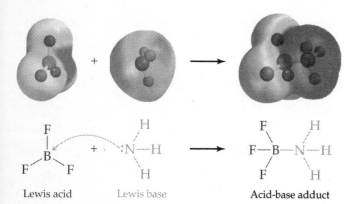

Lewis acid   Lewis base   Acid-base adduct   **FIGURE 15.12** A Lewis acid–base reaction

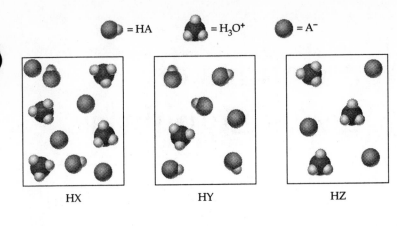

= HA   = H₃O⁺   = A⁻

HX   HY   HZ

Key Concept Question 15.13   The following pictures represent aqueous solutions of three acids HA (A = X, Y, or Z); water molecules have been omitted for clarity:

  (a) Arrange the three acids in order of increasing value of K_a.

  (b) Which acid, if any, is a strong acid?

  (c) Which solution has the highest pH, and which has the lowest pH?

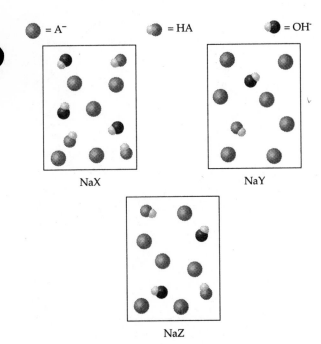

= A⁻   = HA   = OH⁻

NaX   NaY

NaZ

Key Concept Question 15.36   The following pictures represent solutions of three salts NaA (A⁻ = X⁻, Y⁻, or Z⁻); water molecules and Na⁺ ions have been omitted for clarity:

  (a) Arrange the three A⁻ anions in order of increasing base strength.

  (b) Which A⁻ anion has the strongest conjugate acid?

  (c) Why does each box contain the same number of HA molecules and OH⁻ anions?

Chapter 16

Applications of Aqueous Equilibria

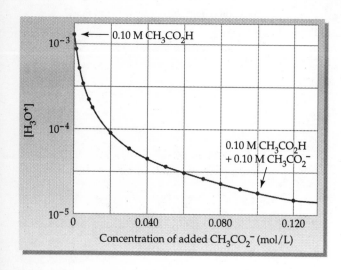

FIGURE 16.2 The common-ion effect

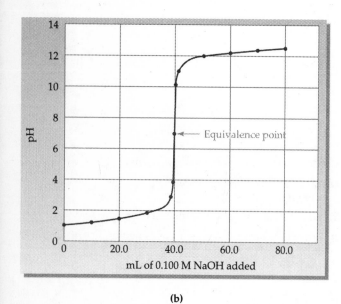

(b)

FIGURE 16.6b pH titration curve: strong acid–strong base

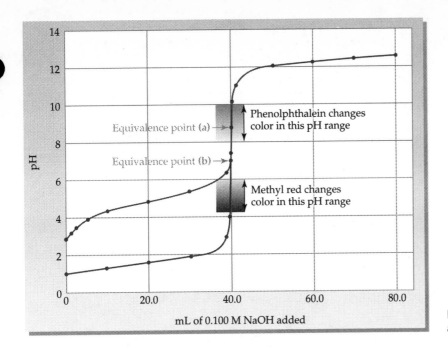

FIGURE 16.7   pH titration curves: weak acid–strong base and strong acid–strong base

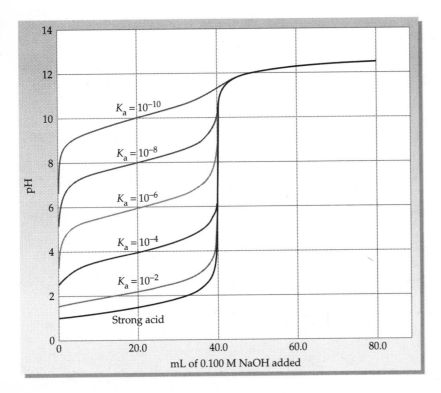

FIGURE 16.8   pH titration curves: weak acid–strong base as a function of K_a

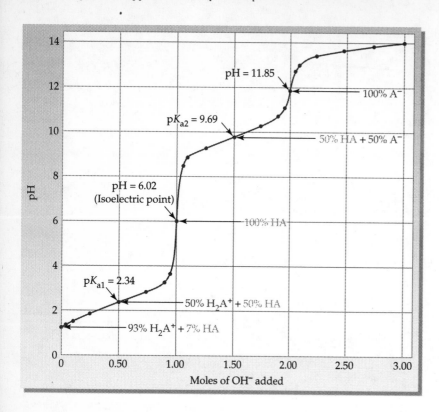

FIGURE 16.10 pH titration curve: polyprotic acid–strong base

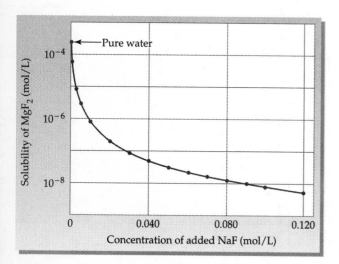

FIGURE 16.11 Common-ion effect on solubility

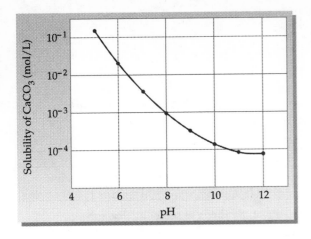

FIGURE 16.12   The effect of pH on solubility

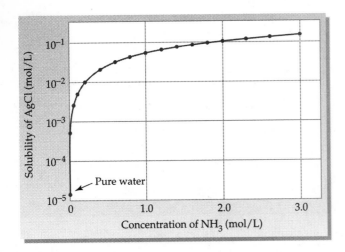

FIGURE 16.14   The effect of complex ion formation on solubility

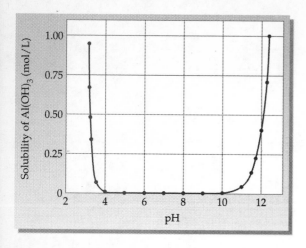

FIGURE 16.16 The effect of pH on the solubility of amphoteric $Al(OH)_3$

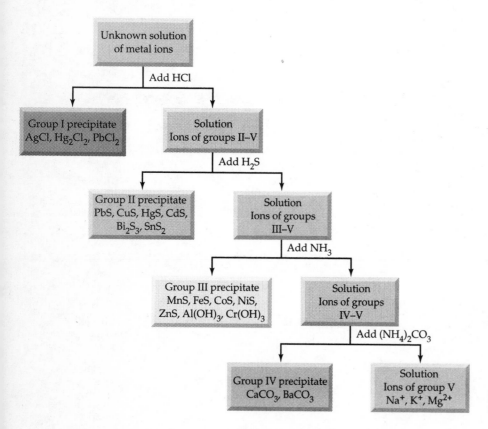

FIGURE 16.17 Qualitative analysis flow chart

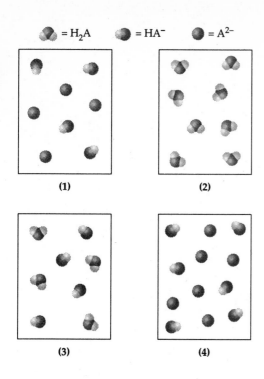

= H$_2$A   = HA$^-$ = A^{2-}

(1)   (2)

(3)   (4)

Key Concept Question 16.34 The following pictures represent solutions that contain one or more of the compounds H$_2$A, NaHA, and Na$_2$A, where H$_2$A is a weak diprotic acid. (Na$^+$ ions and solvent water molecules have been omitted for clarity.)

(a) Which of the solutions are buffer solutions?

(b) Which solution has the greatest buffer capacity?

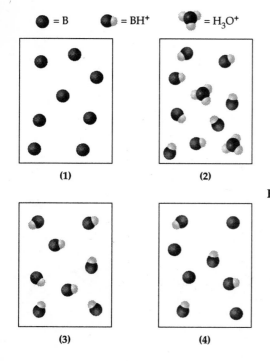

= B   = BH$^+$ = H$_3$O$^+$

(1)   (2)

(3)   (4)

Key Concept Question 16.38 The following pictures represent solutions at various stages in the titration of a weak base B with aqueous HCl. (Cl$^-$ ions and solvent water molecules have been omitted for clarity.)

(a) To which of the following stages do solutions (1)–(4) correspond?

   (i)   The initial solution before addition of any HCl

   (ii) Halfway to the equivalence point

   (iii) At the equivalence point

   (iv) Beyond the equivalence point

(b) Is the pH at the equivalence point more or less than 7?

17

Thermodynamics: Entropy, Free Energy, and Equilibrium

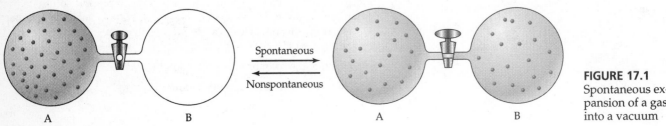

Spontaneous

Nonspontaneous

A   B   A   B

FIGURE 17.1
Spontaneous expansion of a gas into a vacuum

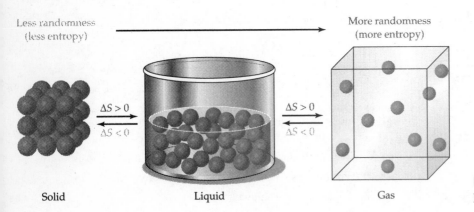

Less randomness (less entropy)

More randomness (more entropy)

$\Delta S > 0$

$\Delta S < 0$

$\Delta S > 0$

$\Delta S < 0$

Solid   Liquid   Gas

FIGURE 17.3   Entropy changes for phase transitions

Less randomness
(less entropy)

More randomness
(more entropy)

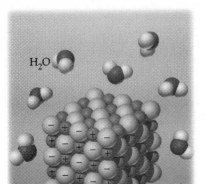
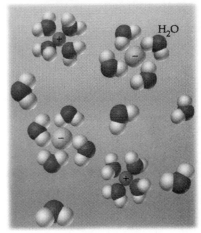

$\Delta S > 0$

$\Delta S < 0$

$NaCl(s) + H_2O(l)$

$Na^+(aq) + Cl^-(aq)$

FIGURE 17.5   Dissolution of NaCl increases entropy

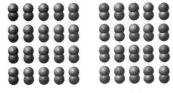

(a)   (b)

FIGURE 17.6   Entropy of ordered and disordered crystals

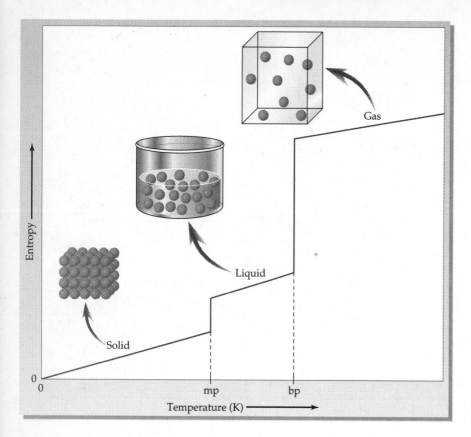

FIGURE 17.8 Entropy versus temperature

TABLE 17.1	Standard Molar Entropies for Some Common Substances at 25°C					
Substance	**Formula**	**$S°$ [J/(K·mol)]**	**Substance**	**Formula**	**$S°$ [J/(K·mol)]**
Gases			**Liquids**		
Acetylene	C_2H_2	200.8	Acetic acid	CH_3CO_2H	160
Ammonia	NH_3	192.3	Ethanol	CH_3CH_2OH	161
Carbon dioxide	CO_2	213.6	Methanol	CH_3OH	127
Carbon monoxide	CO	197.6	Water	H_2O	69.9
Ethylene	C_2H_4	219.5	**Solids**		
Hydrogen	H_2	130.6	Calcium carbonate	$CaCO_3$	92.9
Methane	CH_4	186.2	Calcium oxide	CaO	39.7
Nitrogen	N_2	191.5	Diamond	C	2.4
Nitrogen dioxide	NO_2	240.0	Graphite	C	5.7
Dinitrogen tetroxide	N_2O_4	304.2	Iron	Fe	27.3
Oxygen	O_2	205.0	Iron(III) oxide	Fe_2O_3	87.4

TABLE 17.1 Standard molar entropies at 25°C

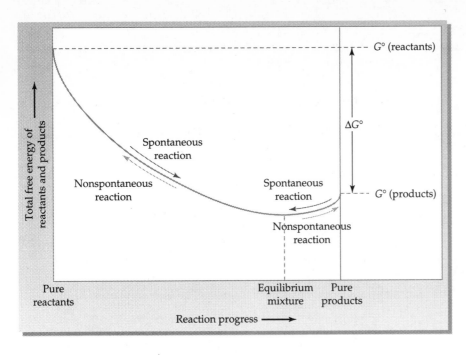

FIGURE 17.10   Total free energy of a reaction mixture versus reaction progress

TABLE 17.3	Standard Free Energies of Formation for Some Common Substances at 25°C					
Substance	**Formula**	$\Delta G°_f$ **(kJ/mol)**	**Substance**	**Formula**	$\Delta G°_f$ **(kJ/mol)**
Gases			**Liquids**		
Acetylene	C_2H_2	209.2	Acetic acid	CH_3CO_2H	−390
Ammonia	NH_3	−16.5	Ethanol	C_2H_5OH	−174.9
Carbon dioxide	CO_2	−394.4	Methanol	CH_3OH	−166.4
Carbon monoxide	CO	−137.2	Water	H_2O	−237.2
Ethylene	C_2H_4	68.1	**Solids**		
Hydrogen	H_2	0	Calcium carbonate	$CaCO_3$	−1128.8
Methane	CH_4	−50.8	Calcium oxide	CaO	−604.0
Nitrogen	N_2	0	Diamond	C	2.9
Nitrogen dioxide	NO_2	51.3	Graphite	C	0
Dinitrogen tetroxide	N_2O_4	97.8	Iron(III) oxide	Fe_2O_3	−742.2

TABLE 17.3   Standard free energies of formation at 25°C

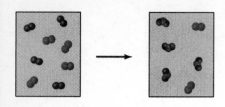

Key Concept Question 17.24 Consider the following spontaneous reaction of A_2 molecules (red) and B_2 molecules (blue):

(a) Write a balanced equation for the reaction.

(b) What are the signs (+, −, or 0) of ΔH, ΔS, and ΔG for the reaction? Explain.

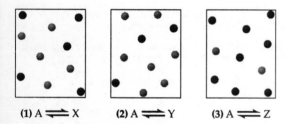

(1) A $\rightleftharpoons$ X   **(2)** A $\rightleftharpoons$ Y   **(3)** A $\rightleftharpoons$ Z

Key Concept Question 17.28 The following pictures represent equilibrium mixtures for the interconversion of A molecules (red) and X, Y, or Z molecules (blue):

What is the sign of $\Delta G°$ for each of the three reactions?

Chapter 18

Electrochemistry

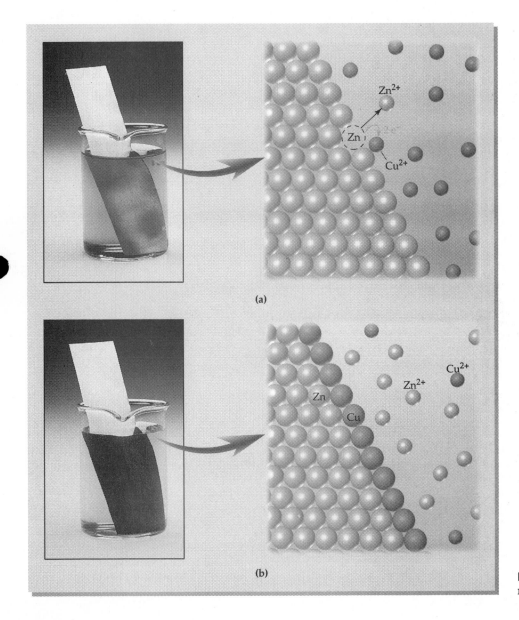

(a)

(b)

FIGURE 18.1 Reaction of zinc metal with aqueous Cu^{2+}

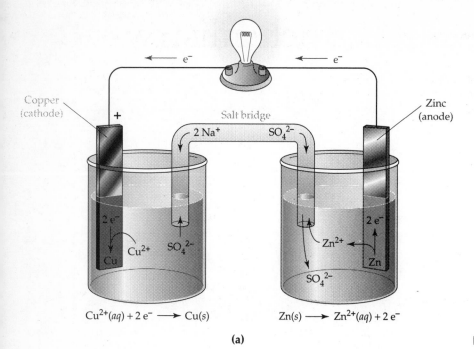

Cu^{2+}(aq) + 2 e$^-$ ⟶ Cu(s)   Zn(s) ⟶ Zn^{2+}(aq) + 2 e$^-$

(a)

FIGURE 18.2A Daniell cell

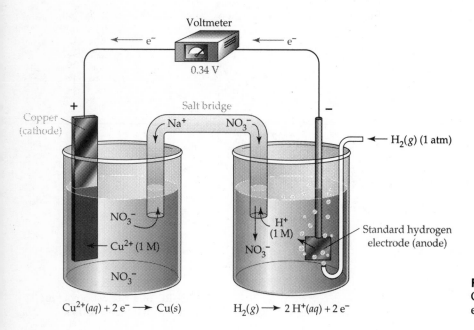

Cu^{2+}(aq) + 2 e$^-$ ⟶ Cu(s)   H$_2$(g) ⟶ 2 H$^+$(aq) + 2 e$^-$

FIGURE 18.4 A galvanic cell with Cu^{2+}/Cu and standard hydrogen electrodes

TABLE 18.1	Standard Reduction Potentials at 25°C	

	Reduction Half-Reaction	$E°$ (V)
	$F_2(g) + 2\,e^- \longrightarrow 2\,F(aq)$	2.87
	$H_2O_2(aq) + 2\,H^+(aq) + 2\,e^- \longrightarrow 2\,H_2O(l)$	1.78
	$MnO_4^-(aq) + 8\,H^+(aq) + 5\,e^- \longrightarrow Mn^{2+}(aq) + 4\,H_2O(l)$	1.51
	$Cl_2(g) + 2\,e^- \longrightarrow 2\,Cl^-(aq)$	1.36
	$Cr_2O_7^{2-}(aq) + 14\,H^+(aq) + 6\,e^- \longrightarrow 2\,Cr^{3+}(aq) + 7\,H_2O(l)$	1.33
	$O_2(g) + 4\,H^+(aq) + 4\,e^- \longrightarrow 2\,H_2O(l)$	1.23
	$Br_2(l) + 2\,e^- \longrightarrow 2\,Br^-(aq)$	1.09
	$Ag^+(aq) + e^- \longrightarrow Ag(s)$	0.80
	$Fe^{3+}(aq) + e^- \longrightarrow Fe^{2+}(aq)$	0.77
	$O_2(g) + 2\,H^+(aq) + 2\,e^- \longrightarrow H_2O_2(aq)$	0.70
	$I_2(s) + 2\,e^- \longrightarrow 2\,I^-(aq)$	0.54
	$O_2(g) + 2\,H_2O(l) + 4\,e^- \longrightarrow 4\,OH^-(aq)$	0.40
	$Cu^{2+}(aq) + 2\,e^- \longrightarrow Cu(s)$	0.34
	$Sn^{4+}(aq) + 2\,e^- \longrightarrow Sn^{2+}(aq)$	0.15
	$2\,H^+(aq) + 2\,e^- \longrightarrow H_2(g)$	0
	$Pb^{2+}(aq) + 2\,e^- \longrightarrow Pb(s)$	−0.13
	$Ni^{2+}(aq) + 2\,e^- \longrightarrow Ni(s)$	−0.26
	$Cd^{2+}(aq) + 2\,e^- \longrightarrow Cd(s)$	−0.40
	$Fe^{2+}(aq) + 2\,e^- \longrightarrow Fe(s)$	−0.45
	$Zn^{2+}(aq) + 2\,e^- \longrightarrow Zn(s)$	−0.76
	$2\,H_2O(l) + 2\,e^- \longrightarrow H_2(g) + 2\,OH^-(aq)$	−0.83
	$Al^{3+}(aq) + 3\,e^- \longrightarrow Al(s)$	−1.66
	$Mg^{2+}(aq) + 2\,e^- \longrightarrow Mg(s)$	−2.37
	$Na^+(aq) + e^- \longrightarrow Na(s)$	−2.71
	$Li^+(aq) + e^- \longrightarrow Li(s)$	−3.04

Stronger oxidizing agent ↑ Weaker oxidizing agent

Weaker reducing agent ↓ Stronger reducing agent

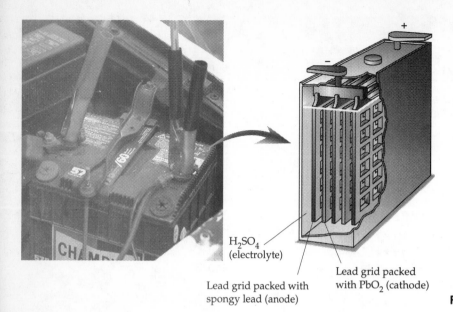

H$_2$SO$_4$
(electrolyte)

Lead grid packed
with PbO$_2$ (cathode)

Lead grid packed with
spongy lead (anode)

FIGURE 18.8 Lead storage battery

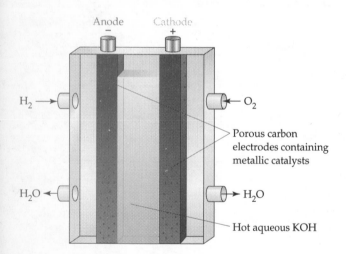

Anode
–

Cathode
+

H$_2$

O$_2$

Porous carbon
electrodes containing
metallic catalysts

H$_2$O

H$_2$O

Hot aqueous KOH

FIGURE 18.12 Hydrogen–oxygen fuel cell

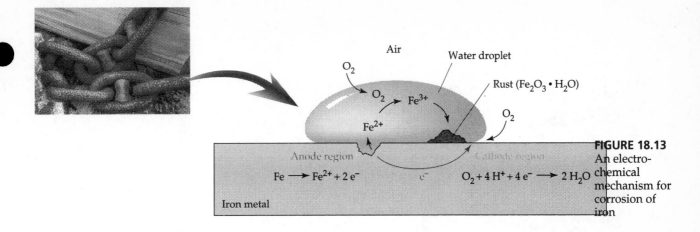

FIGURE 18.13
An electro-chemical mechanism for corrosion of iron

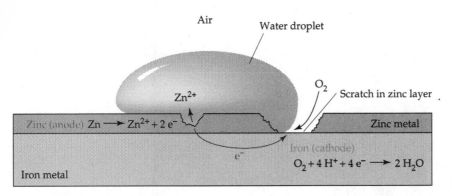

FIGURE 18.14   Cathodic protection

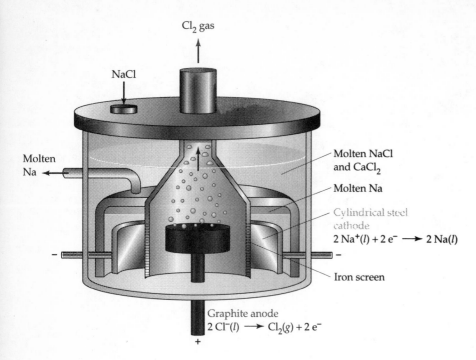

FIGURE 18.16 Downs cell for production of sodium and chlorine

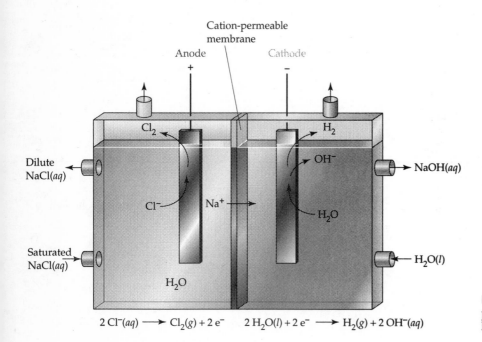

FIGURE 18.17 Membrane cell for production of chlorine and sodium hydroxide

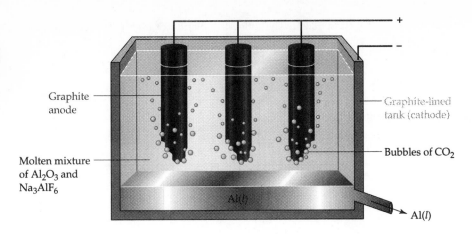

Graphite anode

Molten mixture of Al_2O_3 and Na_3AlF_6

Graphite-lined tank (cathode)

Bubbles of CO_2

Al(*l*)

Al(*l*)

FIGURE 18.18   Electrolytic cell used in the Hall–Heroult process

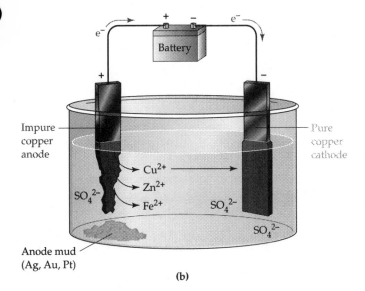

Battery

Impure copper anode

Pure copper cathode

Cu^{2+}

Zn^{2+}

Fe^{2+}

SO_4^{2-}

SO_4^{2-}

SO_4^{2-}

Anode mud (Ag, Au, Pt)

(b)

FIGURE 18.19b   Electrorefining of copper metal

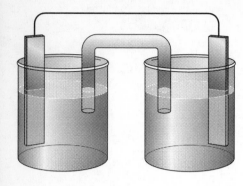

Key Concept Question 18.24 The following picture of a galvanic cell has lead and zinc electrodes:

(a) Label the electrodes, and identify the ions present in the solutions.

(b) Label the anode and cathode.

(c) Indicate the direction of electron flow in the wire and ion flow in the solutions.

(d) Tell what electrolyte could be used in the salt bridge, and indicate the direction of ion flow.

(e) Write balanced equations for the electrode and overall cell reactions.

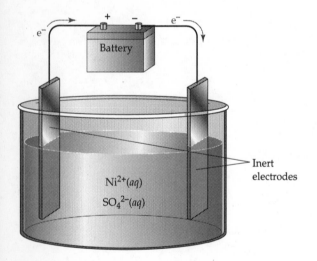

Key Concept Question 18.28 Consider the following electrochemical cell:

(a) Is the cell a galvanic or an electrolytic cell? Explain.

(b) Label the anode and cathode, and show the direction of ion flow.

(c) Write balanced equations for the anode, cathode, and overall cell reactions.

Chapter 19 The Main-Group Elements

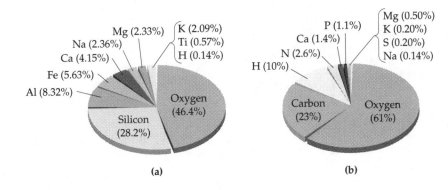

FIGURE 19.1 Most abundant elements in the earth's crust and the human body

TABLE 19.1	The Top 10 Chemicals (2001 U.S. Production)	
Chemical	**Millions of Tons**	**Principal Uses**
Sulfuric acid (H_2SO_4)	40.1	Fertilizers, chemicals, oil refining
Nitrogen (N_2)	35.5	Inert atmospheres, low temperatures
Oxygen (O_2)	26.0	Steelmaking, welding, medical uses
Ethylene ($CH_2{=}CH_2$)	24.8	Plastics, antifreeze
Lime (CaO)	20.6	Steelmaking, chemicals, water treatment
Propylene ($CH_3CH{=}CH_2$)	14.5	Plastics, fibers, solvents
Ammonia (NH_3)	13.0	Fertilizers, nitric acid
Chlorine (Cl_2)	12.0	Chemicals, plastics, water treatment
Phosphoric acid (H_3PO_4)	11.6	Fertilizers, detergents
Sodium hydroxide ($NaOH$)	10.7	Chemicals, textiles, soaps

TABLE 19.1 The top 10 chemicals

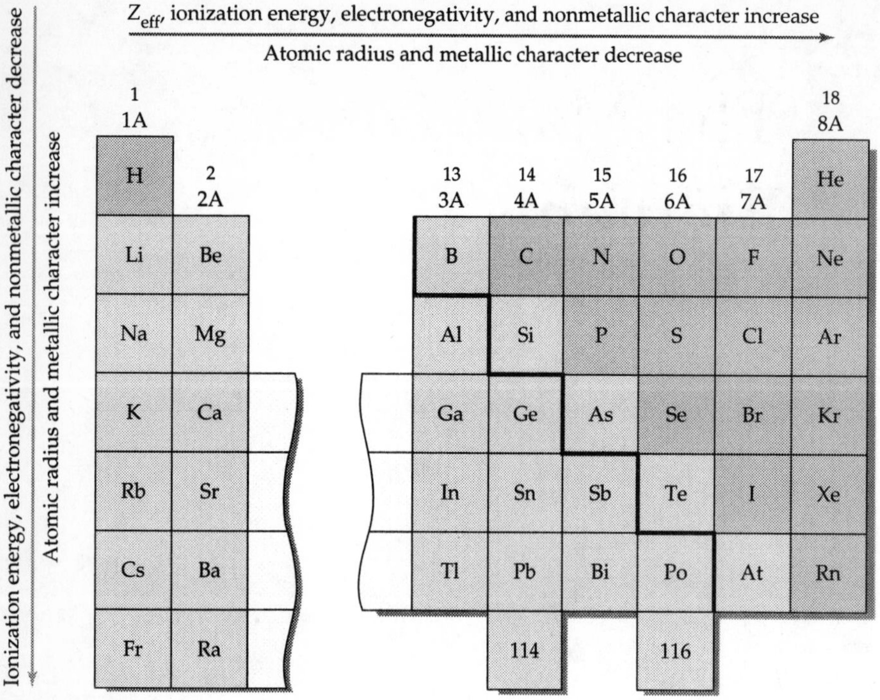

Z_{eff}, ionization energy, electronegativity, and nonmetallic character increase →

Atomic radius and metallic character decrease

Ionization energy, electronegativity, and nonmetallic character decrease ↑

Atomic radius and metallic character increase ↑

1 1A	2 2A		13 3A	14 4A	15 5A	16 6A	17 7A	18 8A
H								He
Li	Be		B	C	N	O	F	Ne
Na	Mg		Al	Si	P	S	Cl	Ar
K	Ca		Ga	Ge	As	Se	Br	Kr
Rb	Sr		In	Sn	Sb	Te	I	Xe
Cs	Ba		Tl	Pb	Bi	Po	At	Rn
Fr	Ra			114		116		

FIGURE 19.2   Periodic trends in properties of main-group elements

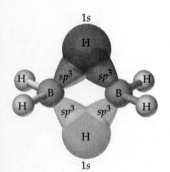

FIGURE 19.3   Three-center bonding in diborane

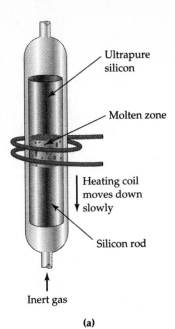

(a)

FIGURE 19.4a   Purification of silicon by zone refining

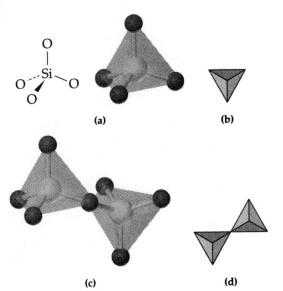

(a)   **(b)**

(c)   **(d)**   **FIGURE 19.5**   The tetrahedral SiO_4 structural unit

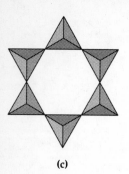

(c)

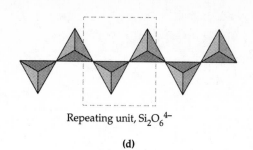

Repeating unit, $Si_2O_6^{4-}$

(d)

FIGURE 19.6c, d Silicate anions with cyclic and chain structures

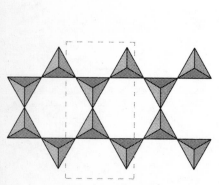

Repeating unit, $Si_4O_{11}^{6-}$

(c)

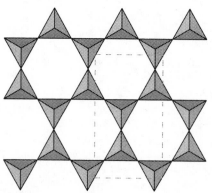

Repeating unit, $Si_4O_{10}^{4-}$

(d)

FIGURE 19.7c, d Double-stranded chain and layer silicate anions

TABLE 19.6	Oxidation States of Nitrogen and Representative Compounds		
Oxidation State	**Compound**	**Formula**	**Electron-Dot Structure**
−3	Ammonia	NH_3	H—N̈—H with H below
−2	Hydrazine	N_2H_4	H—N̈—N̈—H with H, H below
−1	Hydroxylamine	NH_2OH	H—N̈—Ö—H with H below
+1	Nitrous oxide	N_2O	:N≡N—Ö:
+2	Nitric oxide	NO	:Ṅ=Ö:
+3	Nitrous acid	HNO_2	H—Ö—N̈=Ö:
+4	Nitrogen dioxide	NO_2	:Ö—Ṅ=Ö:
+5	Nitric acid	HNO_3	H—Ö—N=Ö: with :Ö: below

TABLE 19.6 Oxidation states of nitrogen and representative compounds

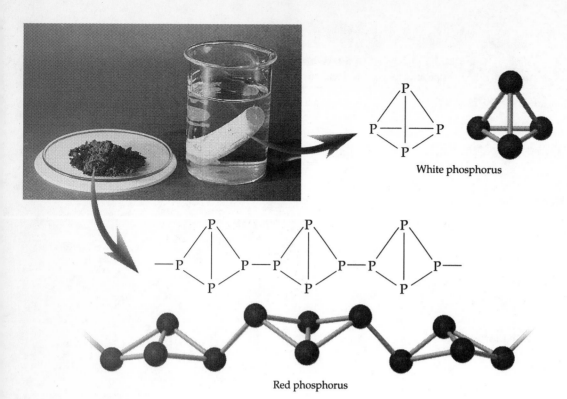

White phosphorus

Red phosphorus

FIGURE 19.9
Structures of white
and red phosphorus

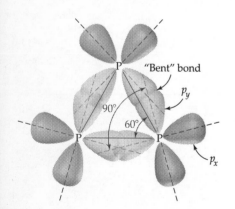

FIGURE 19.10   Bent bonds in white phosphorus

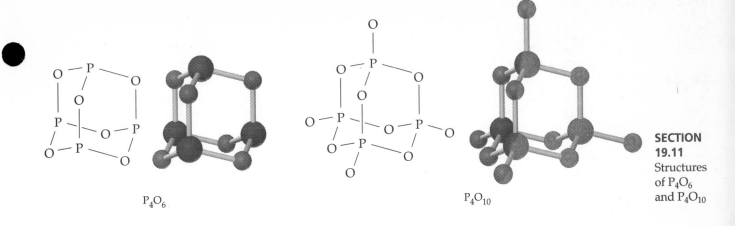

P_4O_6

P_4O_{10}

SECTION 19.11 Structures of P_4O_6 and P_4O_{10}

(a)

(b)

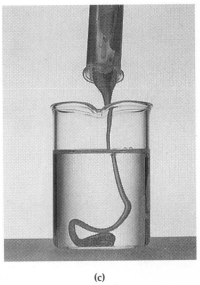

(c)

FIGURE 19.11 Effect of temperature on the properties of sulfur

Key Concept Question 19.16   Consider the six second- and third-row elements in groups 5A–7A of the periodic table:

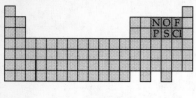

Possible molecular structures for common allotropes of these elements are shown below

(a) What is the molecular structure of each of the six elements?

(b) Using electron-dot structures, explain why each element has its particular molecular structure.

(c) Explain why nitrogen and phosphorus have different molecular structures and why oxygen and sulfur have different molecular structures, but fluorine and chlorine have the same molecular structure.

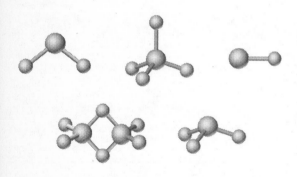

Key Concept Question 19.18   The following models represent the structures of binary hydrides of second-row elements:

(a) Identify the nonhydrogen atom in each case, and write the molecular formula for each hydride.

(b) Draw an electron-dot structure for each hydride. For which hydride is there a problem in drawing the structure? Explain.

Chapter 20

Transition Elements and Coordination Chemistry

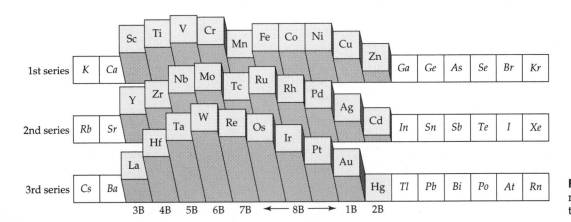

FIGURE 20.2 Relative melting points of transition elements

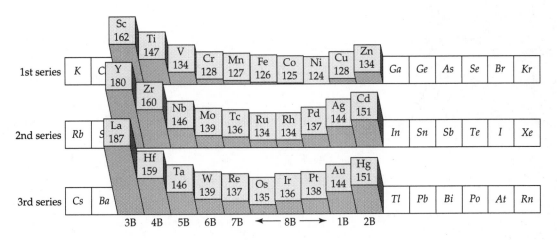

FIGURE 20.3 Atomic radii of transition elements

1st series	K	Ca	Sc	Ti	V	Cr	Mn	Fe	Co	Ni	Cu	Zn	Ga	Ge	As	Se	Br	Kr

2nd series	Rb	Sr	Y	Zr	Nb	Mo	Tc	Ru	Rh	Pd	Ag	Cd	In	Sn	Sb	Te	I	Xe

3rd series	Cs	Ba	La	Hf	Ta	W	Re	Os	Ir	Pt	Au	Hg	Tl	Pb	Bi	Po	At	Rn

3B 4B 5B 6B 7B ←— 8B —→ 1B 2B

FIGURE 20.5 Relative densities of transition elements

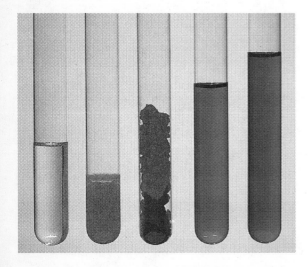

SECTION 20.3 Compounds of manganese in different oxidation states

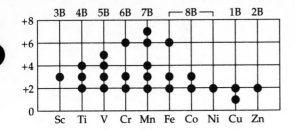

FIGURE 20.6 Common oxidation states for first-series transition elements

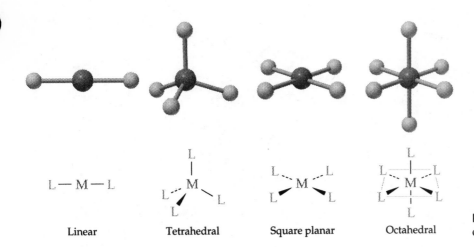

| Linear | Tetrahedral | Square planar | Octahedral |

FIGURE 20.12 Coordination geometries of ML_n complexes

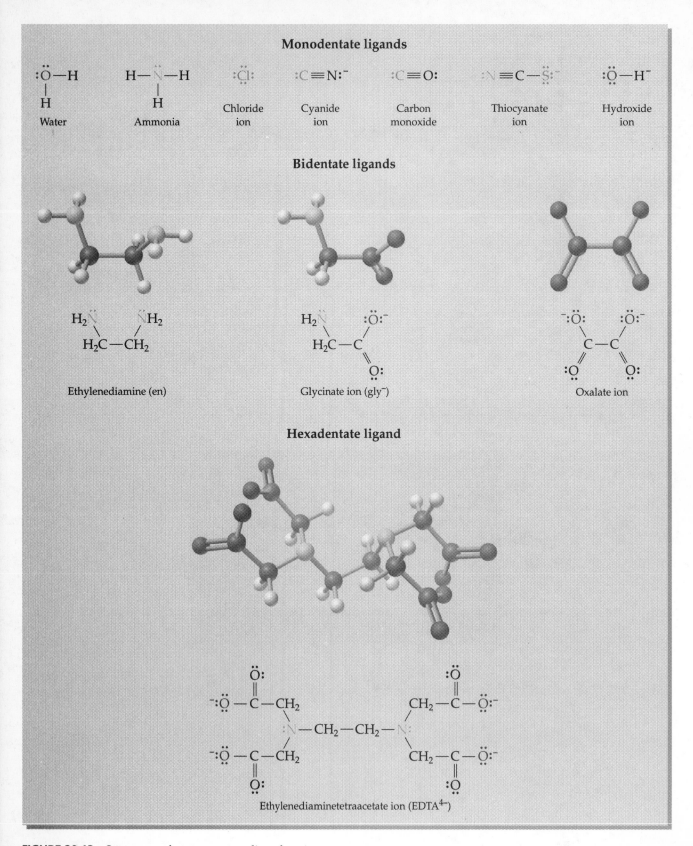

FIGURE 20.13   Structures of some common ligands

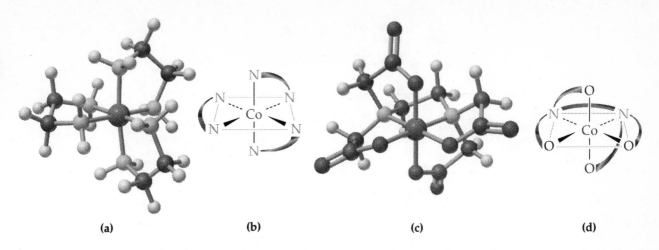

(a)   (b)   (c)   (d)

FIGURE 20.14 Structures of $[Co(en)_3]^{3+}$ and $[Co(EDTA)]^-$

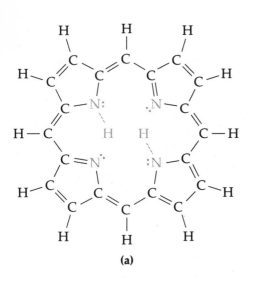

(a)

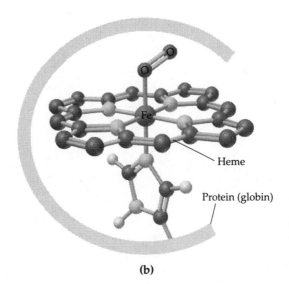

(b)

FIGURE 20.15 The porphine molecule and heme group in oxyhemoglobin

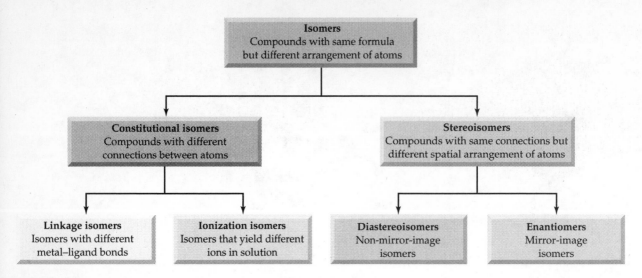

FIGURE 20.16 Classification of isomers in coordination chemistry

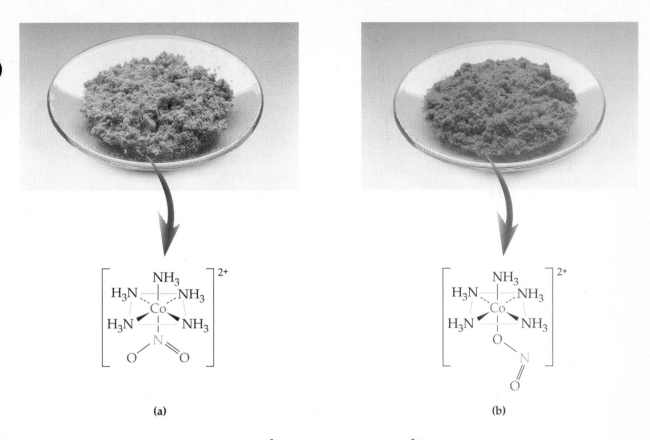

(a)   (b)

FIGURE 20.17   Structures of $[Co(NH_3)_5(NO_2)]^{2+}$ and $[Co(NH_3)_5(ONO)]^{2+}$ linkage isomers

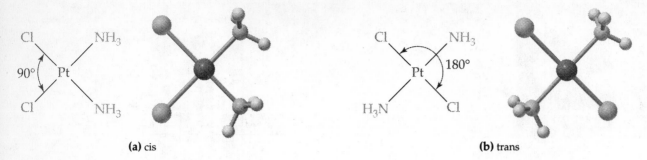

FIGURE 20.18   Diastereoisomers of $Pt(NH_3)_2Cl_2$

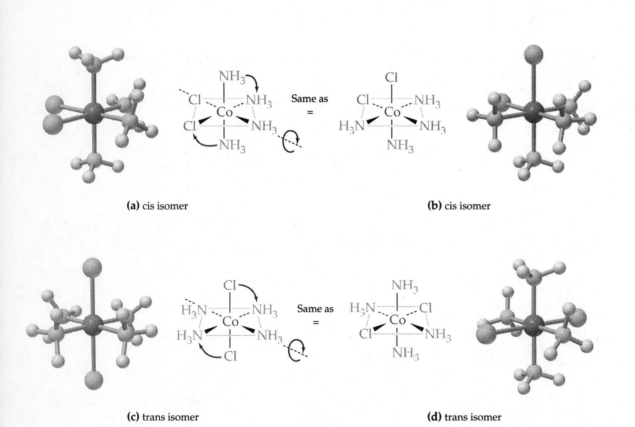

FIGURE 20.19   Diastereoisomers of the $[Co(NH_3)_4Cl_2]^+$ ion

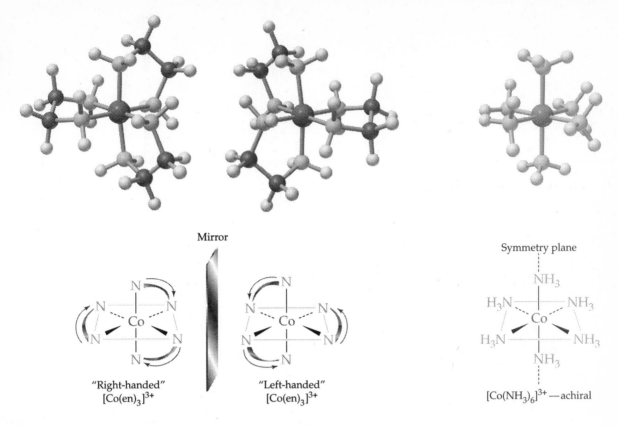

FIGURE 20.21 Structures of $[Co(en)_3]^{3+}$ enantiomers and $[Co(NH_3)_6]^{3+}$

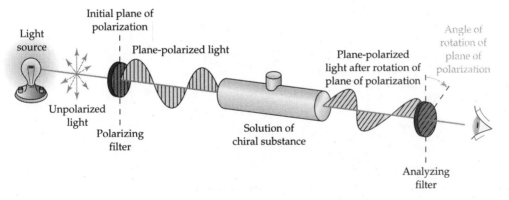

FIGURE 20.22 A polarimeter

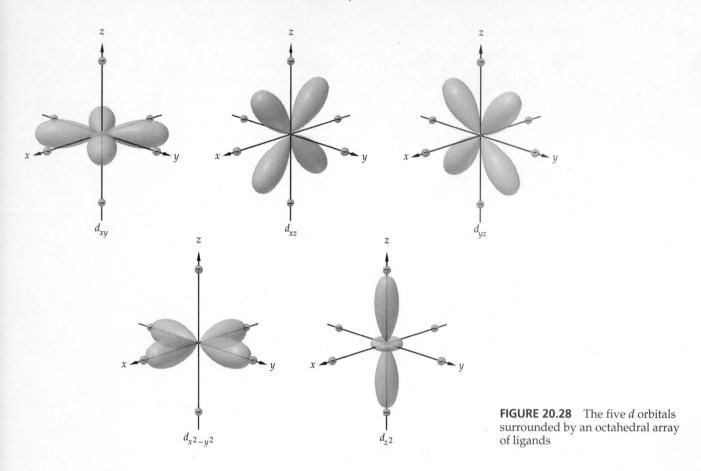

FIGURE 20.28   The five d orbitals surrounded by an octahedral array of ligands

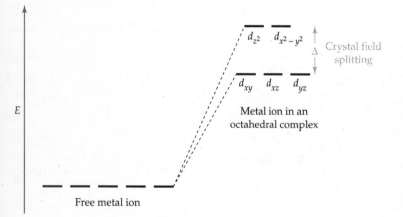

FIGURE 20.29 d-orbital energy level diagram for an octahedral complex

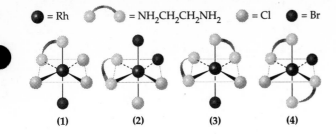

● = Rh ⬭ = NH₂CH₂CH₂NH₂ ● = Cl ● = Br

(1)   (2)   (3)   (4)

Key Concept Question 20.11 Consider the following ethylenediamine complexes of rhodium:

(a) Which complexes are chiral, and which are achiral?

(b) Draw the enantiomer of each chiral complex.

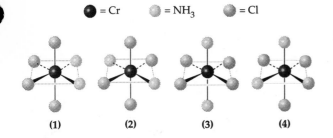

● = Cr ● = NH₃ ● = Cl

(1)   (2)   (3)   (4)

Key Concept Question 20.22 Consider the following isomers of $[Cr(NH_3)_2Cl_4]^-$:

(a) Label the isomers as cis or trans.

(b) Which isomers are identical, and which are different?

(c) Do any of these isomers exist as enantiomers? Explain.

Chapter 21

Metals and Solid-State Materials

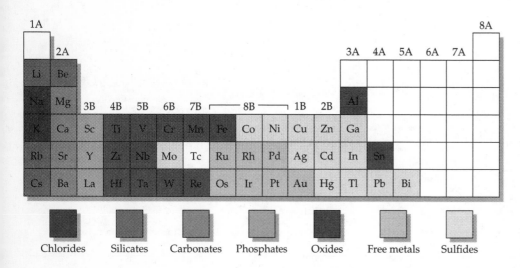

FIGURE 21.2 Primary mineral sources of metals

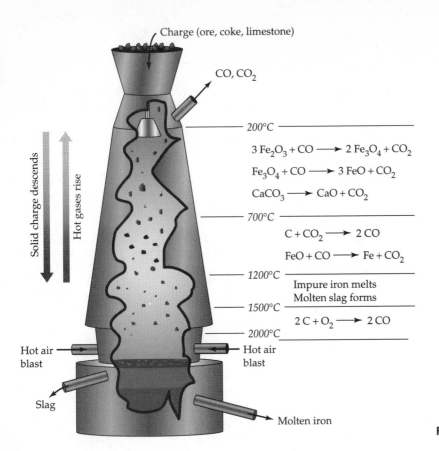

Charge (ore, coke, limestone)

CO, CO_2

Solid charge descends

Hot gases rise

200°C

$3 Fe_2O_3 + CO \longrightarrow 2 Fe_3O_4 + CO_2$

$Fe_3O_4 + CO \longrightarrow 3 FeO + CO_2$

$CaCO_3 \longrightarrow CaO + CO_2$

700°C

$C + CO_2 \longrightarrow 2 CO$

$FeO + CO \longrightarrow Fe + CO_2$

1200°C

Impure iron melts
Molten slag forms

1500°C

$2 C + O_2 \longrightarrow 2 CO$

2000°C

Hot air blast

Hot air blast

Slag

Molten iron

FIGURE 21.5   Blast furnace

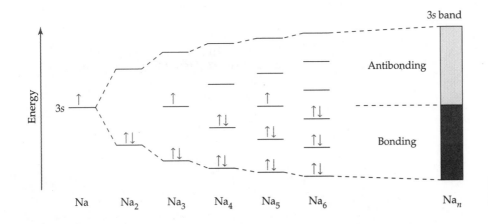

Energy

3s band

Antibonding

3s

Bonding

Na Na_2 Na_3 Na_4 Na_5 Na_6 Na_n

FIGURE 21.7   MO energy levels for Na_n molecules

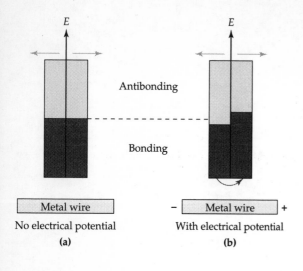

No electrical potential

(a)

With electrical potential

(b)

FIGURE 21.8 Population of energy levels for a one-dimensional sodium wire

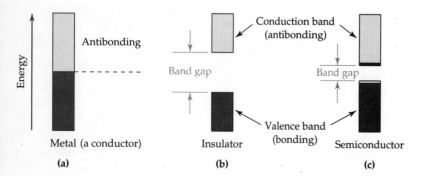

Metal (a conductor)

(a)

Insulator

(b)

Semiconductor

(c)

Figure 21.10 Bands of MO energy levels for a metal, an insulator, and a semiconductor

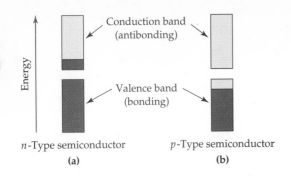

n-Type semiconductor

(a)

p-Type semiconductor

(b)

FIGURE 21.11   MO energy levels for doped semiconductors

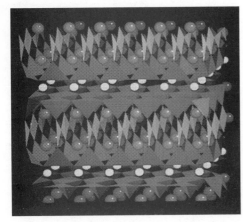

FIGURE 21.13   Crystal structure of $YBa_2Cu_3O_7$

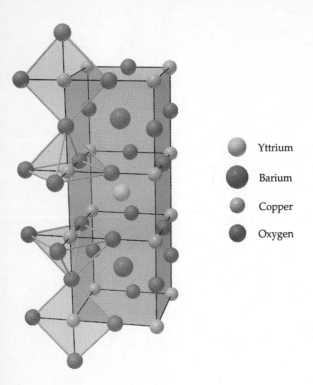

Yttrium

Barium

Copper

Oxygen

FIGURE 21.14   One unit cell of $YBa_2Cu_3O_7$

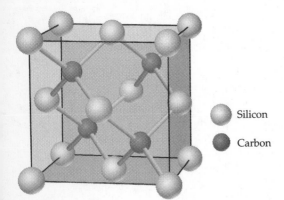

Silicon

Carbon

FIGURE 21.17   Unit cell of silicon carbide

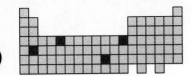

Key Concept Question 21.12   Look at the location of elements A, B, C, and D in the following periodic table:

Without looking at Figure 21.2, predict whether these elements are likely to be found in nature as carbonates, oxides, sulfides, or in uncombined form. Explain.

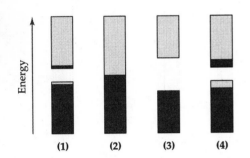

Key Concept Question 21.14   The following pictures show the electron populations of the bands of MO energy levels for four different materials:

(a) Classify each material as an insulator, a semiconductor, or a metal.

(b) Arrange the four materials in order of increasing electrical conductivity. Explain.

(c) Tell whether the conductivity of each material increases or decreases when the temperature increases.

Chapter 22

Nuclear Chemistry

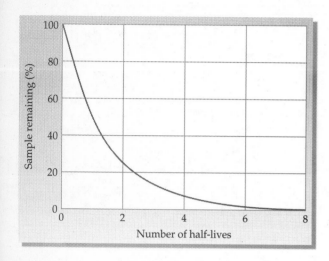

FIGURE 22.2 Radioactive decay rate

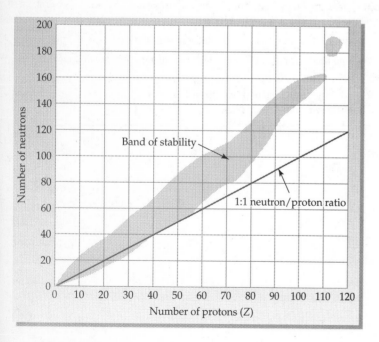

FIGURE 22.3 Band of nuclear stability

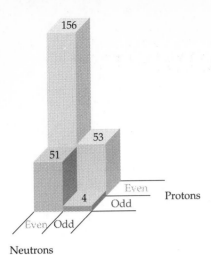

FIGURE 22.4   Odd/even neutron/proton combinations

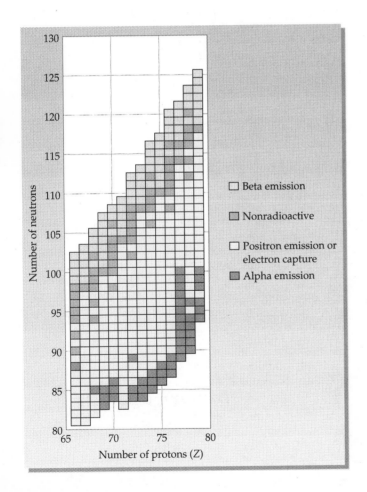

FIGURE 22.5   Close-up of band of nuclear stability

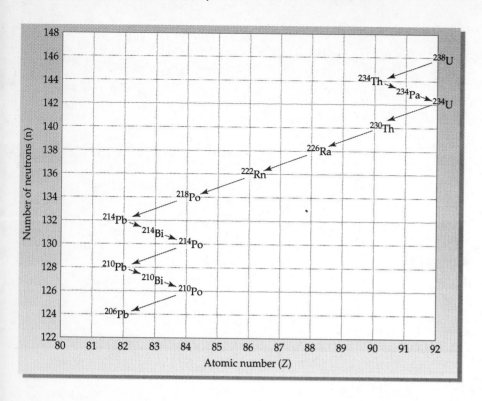

FIGURE 22.6   Uranium-238 decay series

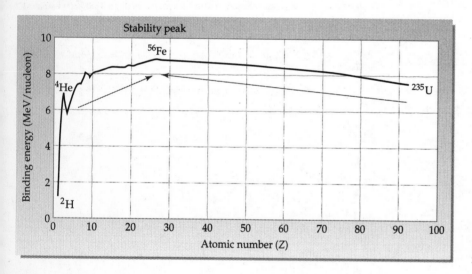

FIGURE 22.7   Binding energy per nucleon

Key Concept Question 22.19 $^{40}_{19}K$ decays by positron emission to give $^{40}_{18}Ar$. If yellow spheres represent $^{40}_{19}K$ atoms and blue spheres represent $^{40}_{18}Ar$ atoms, how many half-lives have passed in the following sample?

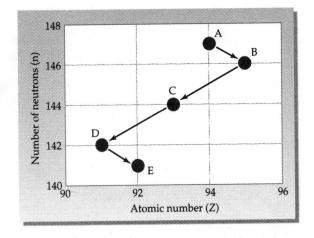

Key Concept Question 22.22   Isotope A decays to isotope E through the series of steps shown in the graph. The series has two kinds of processes: one represented by the shorter arrows pointing right and the other represented by the longer arrows pointing left.

(a) What kind of nuclear decay process does each kind of arrow correspond to?

(b) Identify and write the symbol $^A_Z X$ for each isotope in the decay series:

Chapter 23

Organic Chemistry

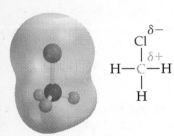

Chloromethane, CH₃Cl
(electron-poor carbon)

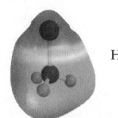

Methyllithium, CH₃Li
(electron-rich carbon)

SECTION 23.1   Electrostatic potential maps of CH_3Cl and CH_3Li

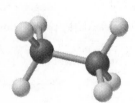

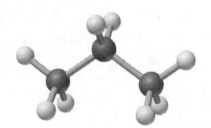

Methane, CH₄

Ethane, C₂H₆

Propane, C₃H₈

SECTION 23.2   Models of methane, ethane, and propane

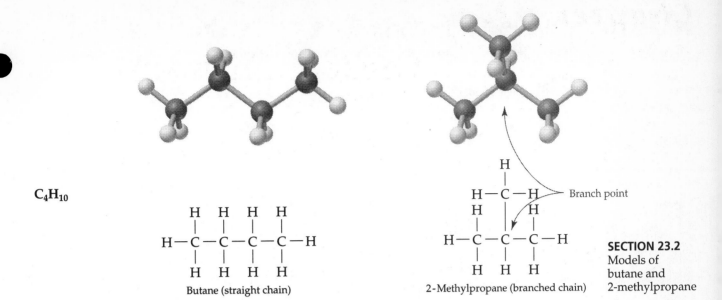

C_4H_{10}

Butane (straight chain)

2-Methylpropane (branched chain)

Branch point

SECTION 23.2
Models of
butane and
2-methylpropane

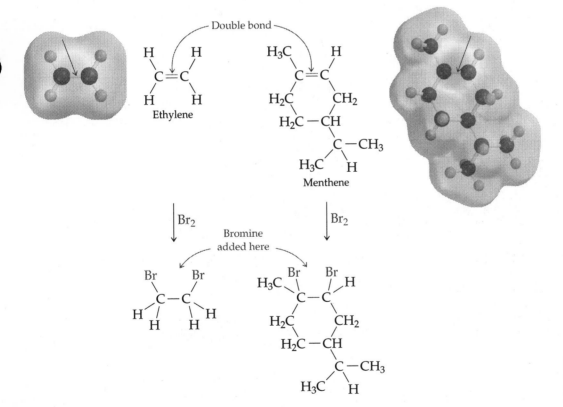

Double bond

Ethylene

Menthene

Bromine
added here

FIGURE 23.1 Reactions
of ethylene and men-
thene with bromine

TABLE 23.2 Some Important Families of Organic Molecules

Family Name	Functional Group Structure	Simple Example	Name	Name Ending
Alkane	(contains only C—H and C—C single bonds)	CH_3CH_3	Ethane	-ane
Alkene	$\text{C}=\text{C}$	$H_2C=CH_2$	Ethene (Ethylene)	-ene
Alkyne	$—C\equiv C—$	$H—C\equiv C—H$	Ethyne (Acetylene)	-yne
Arene (aromatic)	(benzene ring structure)	Benzene	Benzene	None
Alcohol	$—\overset{\|}{\underset{\|}{C}}—O—H$	CH_3OH	Methanol	-ol
Ether	$—\overset{\|}{\underset{\|}{C}}—O—\overset{\|}{\underset{\|}{C}}—$	CH_3OCH_3	Dimethyl ether	ether
Amine	$—\overset{\|}{\underset{\|}{C}}—N—$	CH_3NH_2	Methylamine	-amine
Aldehyde	$—\overset{\|}{\underset{\|}{C}}—\overset{O}{\overset{\|}{C}}—H$	$CH_3\overset{O}{\overset{\|}{C}}H$	Ethanal (Acetaldehyde)	-al
Ketone	$—\overset{\|}{\underset{\|}{C}}—\overset{O}{\overset{\|}{C}}—\overset{\|}{\underset{\|}{C}}—$	$CH_3\overset{O}{\overset{\|}{C}}CH_3$	Propanone (Acetone)	-one
Carboxylic acid	$—\overset{\|}{\underset{\|}{C}}—\overset{O}{\overset{\|}{C}}—O—H$	$CH_3\overset{O}{\overset{\|}{C}}OH$	Ethanoic acid (Acetic acid)	-oic acid
Ester	$—\overset{\|}{\underset{\|}{C}}—\overset{O}{\overset{\|}{C}}—O—\overset{\|}{\underset{\|}{C}}—$	$CH_3\overset{O}{\overset{\|}{C}}OCH_3$	Methyl ethanoate (Methyl acetate)	-oate
Amide	$—\overset{\|}{\underset{\|}{C}}—\overset{O}{\overset{\|}{C}}—N—$	$CH_3\overset{O}{\overset{\|}{C}}NH_2$	Ethanamide (Acetamide)	-amide

*The bonds whose connections aren't specified are assumed to be attached to carbon or hydrogen atoms in the rest of the molecule.

TABLE 23.2 Table of functional groups

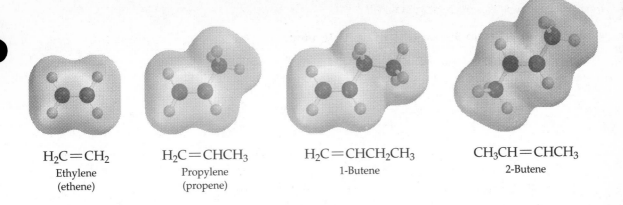

$H_2C{=}CH_2$
Ethylene
(ethene)

$H_2C{=}CHCH_3$
Propylene
(propene)

$H_2C{=}CHCH_2CH_3$
1-Butene

$CH_3CH{=}CHCH_3$
2-Butene

SECTION 23.9 Electrostatic potential maps of ethylene, propylene,1-butene, and 2-butene

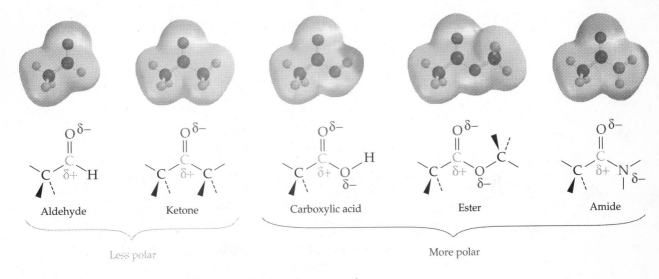

Aldehyde Ketone Carboxylic acid Ester Amide

Less polar   More polar

FIGURE 23.5 Electrostatic potential maps of carbonyl compounds

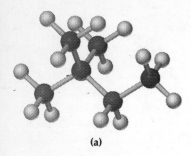

(a)

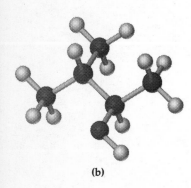

(b)

Key Concept Question 23.30 Convert each of the following models into a condensed formula:

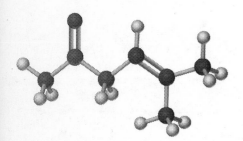

Key Concept Question 23.36 Draw two isomers of the following compound:

Chapter 24

Biochemistry

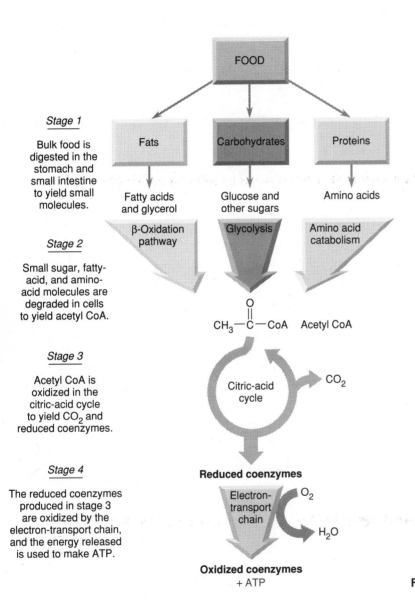

Stage 1

Bulk food is digested in the stomach and small intestine to yield small molecules.

Stage 2

Small sugar, fatty-acid, and amino-acid molecules are degraded in cells to yield acetyl CoA.

Stage 3

Acetyl CoA is oxidized in the citric-acid cycle to yield CO_2 and reduced coenzymes.

Stage 4

The reduced coenzymes produced in stage 3 are oxidized by the electron-transport chain, and the energy released is used to make ATP.

FIGURE 24.1 Catabolic pathways

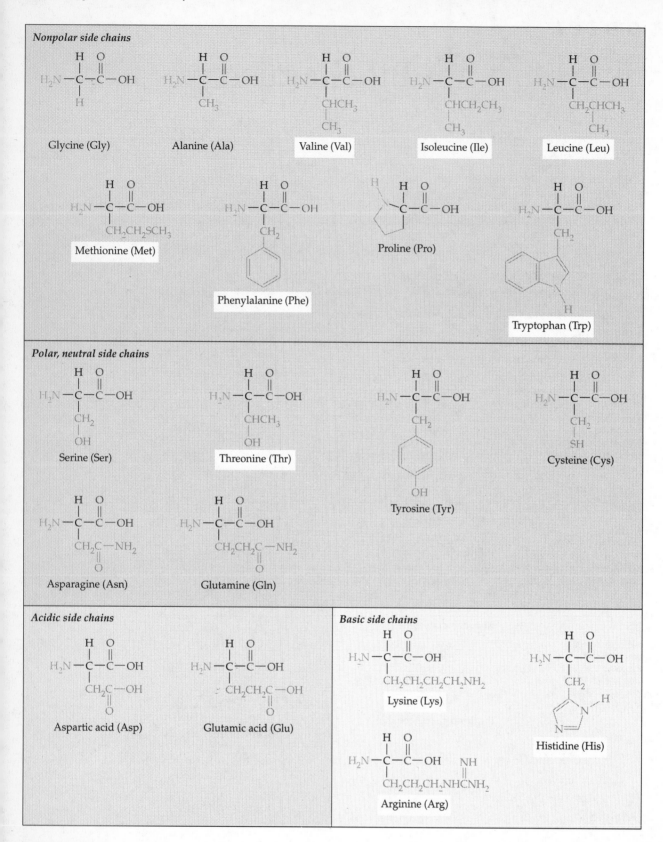

FIGURE 24.2 Structures of the 20 α-amino acids in proteins

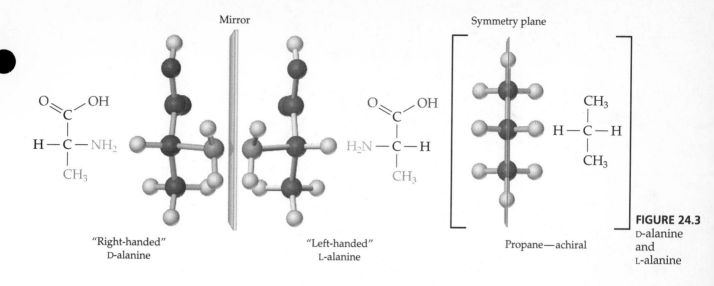

Mirror

Symmetry plane

"Right-handed"
D-alanine

"Left-handed"
L-alanine

Propane—achiral

FIGURE 24.3
D-alanine
and
L-alanine

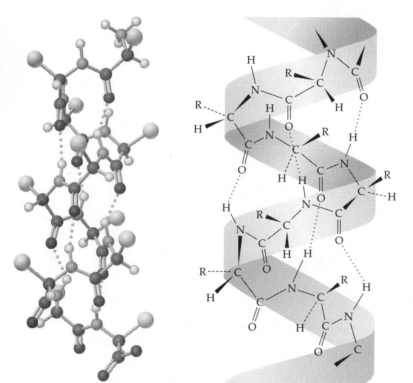

Figure 24.7 α-helical secondary structure of keratin

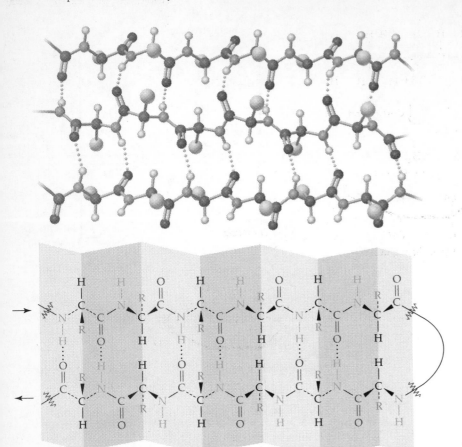

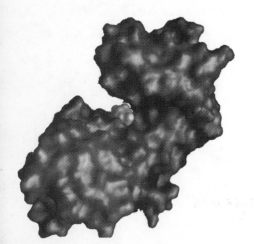

FIGURE 24.8 β-pleated-sheet secondary structure of silk fibroin

FIGURE 24.10 Lock-and-key model of enzyme action

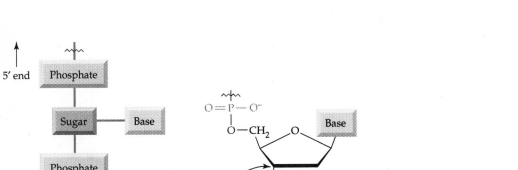

Open-chain glucose

α-Glucose

β-Glucose

FIGURE 24.12
Cyclic α and β forms
of glucose

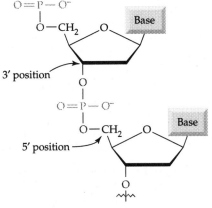

FIGURE 24.16   Generalized structure of a
nucleic acid

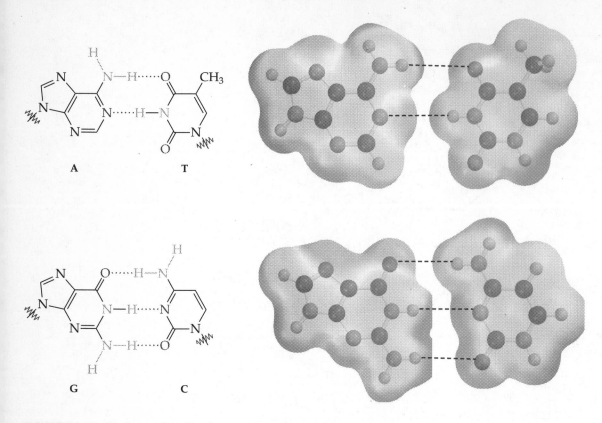

FIGURE 24.17   Hydrogen bonding between base pairs in DNA

FIGURE 24.18   The DNA double helix

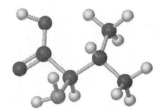

Key Concept Question 24.27   Does the following model represent a D-amino acid or an L-amino acid? Identify it.

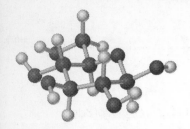

Key Concept Question 24.28 Is the following model of glucose in the α form or the β form?

Photo Credits

Chapter 1

Page 3: Figure 1.7, Faint, Grant V/Getty Images Inc. - Image Bank.

Chapter 2

Page 5: Figure 2.3, Richard Megna/Fundamental Photographs.
Page 5: Figure 2.3, Richard Megna/Fundamental Photographs.
Page 7: Figure 2.10, Richard M. Busch/Richard M. Busch.

Chapter 4

Page 14: Figure 4.2, Peticolas/Megna/Fundamental Photographs.
Page 14: Figure 4.2, Kip Peticolas & Richard Megna/ Fundamental Photographs.

Chapter 8

Page 47: Figure 8.13, D. Van Kirk/Getty Images Inc. - Image Bank.
Page 47: Figure 8.13, Frank Spinelli/Getty Images Inc. - Stone Allstock.
Page 47: Figure 8.13, Ezio Geneletti/Getty Images Inc. - Image Bank.

Chapter 9

Page 50: Table 9.2, Richard Megna/Fundamental Photographs.
Page 51: Table 9.3, William Johnson/Stock Boston.

Chapter 10

Page 58: Figure 10.8, Tom Pantages/Tom Pantages.
Page 59: Figure 10.10, Ed Degginger/Color-Pic, Inc.
Page 65: Figure 10.26, General Electric Corporate Research & Development Center.

Chapter 18

Page 109: Figure 18.1, Richard Megna/Fundamental Photographs.
Page 109: Figure 18.1, Richard Megna/Fundamental Photographs.
Page 112: Figure 18.8, Liz Strenk/Super Stock, Inc.
Page 113: Figure 18.13, Zandria Muench/Getty Images Inc. - Stone Allstock.

Chapter 19

Page 122: Figure 19.9, Richard Megna/Fundamental Photographs.
Page 123: Figure 19.11, Richard Megna/Fundamental Photographs.
Page 123: Figure 19.11, Richard Megna/Fundamental Photographs.
Page 123: Figure 19.11, Richard Megna/Fundamental Photographs.

Chapter 20

Page 126: Figure 20.3, Richard Megna/Fundamental Photographs.
Page 127: Figure 20.17, Richard Megna/Fundamental Photographs.
Page 127: Figure 20.17, Richard Megna/Fundamental Photographs.

Chapter 21

Page 139: Figure 21.13, Chemical Design Ltd./Science Photo Library/Photo Researchers, Inc.

Chapter 24

Page 154: Figure 24.10, Ken Edward/Biografix/Science Source/ Photo Researchers, Inc.
Page 157: Figure 24.18, Michael Freeman/Phototake NYC.